PAISLEY
PUBLIC LIBRARY
Central Library, High Street,
Telephone: PAIsley 2360

HOURS OF OPENING

Monday, Tuesday,
Thursday and Friday
10 a.m. — 8 p.m.

Wednesday and Saturday
10 a.m. — 5 p.m.

RESERVE

FINES:—Fines for detention
will be charged according to
the bye-laws.

RENEWALS:—Period of loan
may be renewed if the book
is not required by another
borrower

**BOOKS DAMAGED OR
LOST:**—Readers are required
to take care of books issued
to them. Loss or damage
must be made good and the
value of books lost or
damaged will be charged.

**This book is due for return
on latest date stamped on
card.**

**PLEASE DO NOT REMOVE
CARD**—6d. fine will be
charged if lost.

THE END OF
THE RAINBOW

BY

BEE JAY

(Author of *And It Came to Pass*)

BARKER JOHNSON

STRATH · GAIRLOCH · ROSS-SHIRE

1964

PRINTED IN GREAT BRITAIN
BY R. & R. CLARK, LTD., EDINBURGH

FOREWORD

THIS is a romantic story ; not so much as one romance, but three—a trilogy—with locations in Ceylon, Egypt and Scotland ; and for those who are particularly interested in Scotland, it deals fully with that delightful island, THE ISLE OF MULL ; concluding with Gairloch in Wester Ross ; Highland life and pathos to the full. . . .

It may be read as a fitting companion to *And It Came to Pass*, which pivoted mainly on Gairloch and the Isle of Skye—and which was spoken of as a 'book with a difference'. It is hoped this novel will be one classified in that vein also ; and that it will afford pleasant reading.

To those who like love stories of a somewhat different nature than those usually found on most bookstalls, this book should have a direct appeal. It is not so much a 'boy-meets-girl' romance, but rather it is of a more matured character, though admittedly set at the commencement in colourful, romantic surroundings in sun-drenched Ceylon. From thence it passes through Egypt, the wonders of the desert and the pyramids ; and latterly draws to Mull before eventually anchoring in Gairloch, 'God's own country'. Such is the story.

All characters in the story proper are purely imaginary.

This is a story that could happen to any one of us.

Mull is certainly a lovely island, and those who go over the sea from Oban to spend a few days there will wish to return again, and yet again ; for Mull is a sparsely populated island, and with a winding coast-line of some 300 miles, it is an ideal island for visitors who look for peace and quiet and to be away from the hurly-burly of town routine.

This book should be of invaluable help to those making the journey, as pains have been taken to give tourists much of the information they seek in visiting that island.

All the world loves a lover ; and these forthcoming pages— from the pen of an Englishman (a Colonial) living in Gairloch's wonderland—will, it is thought, combine both lovable as well as 'down-to-earth' reading.

Libraries say 'romance' is still the favourite subject of most women—and of not a few men! *Slàinte Mhath !*

Of a truth, 'whatever will be, will be'.

GAIRLOCH, 1964   S. B. J.

CONTENTS

*Dedicated
to Fiona ; for how could it
be otherwise?*

CHAPTER I

EARLY YEARS

WHEN, as son and heir, I first saw the light of day—towards the end of the 19th century in a small house in an East Yorkshire town—I was christened Stanley. Not a very common name, and as I became older, I remember asking my parents 'Why Stanley?'

It would appear at that time, the name of Dr. David Livingstone was still in everyone's mind; Livingstone (born 19th March 1813 in a one-room house in a Blantyre, Lanarkshire, tenement), the great Scots explorer and missionary, discoverer of the Victoria Falls of the Zambezi in 1855; and H. M. Stanley, who was a celebrated journalist (and later an African explorer), set out towards his later life—some ninety years ago—on his epic journey to discover the whereabouts of Livingstone. We all know, I think, of Stanley's journey, with all its horrors undertaken primarily to make a newspaper sensation (the *New York Herald*), and of his suddenly coming across Livingstone in a clearing in the wilds of darkest Africa; of the two walking towards each other, and of Stanley's famous phrase, 'Dr. Livingstone, I presume?' This, accompanied by the polite raising of hats—or, as it would be out there, topees or pith sun-helmets. And so, as I understood it rightly, when my father said to my mother, 'What shall we call him?' she replied meekly in a soft, faint voice, 'Let's call him Stanley'.

And so it came to pass—'Stanley', after the great explorer; or maybe after Sir Walter Scott's, 'On Stanley on, were the last words of Marmion'—although that great Scots writer had died sixty years previous.

Stanley was knighted in 1899 for his explorations and writings. Livingstone died 1st May 1873 and was buried in Westminster Abbey. As regards myself, the term 'explorer' in after years became an apt one; for, as readers will see later, I covered both the Far and the Near East in the comparatively early part of my life; and my explorations there led me into endless variety and endless 'charm'.

The vicissitudes and habits of the Orient, however, demanded firm control of oneself, in living a life according to my strict upbringings ; for in my youth we still lived in Queen Victoria's age. Queen Victoria of Great Britain and Empress of India ; although her 'sixty glorious years' ended in 1901.

I grew up—as indeed all healthy babies do—and my very young days at a private kindergarten school (few of any such exist these days) passed uneventfully ; and then came lessons the hard way. As we had migrated to a country district, the one and only school was a Board School ; one would now term it, I suppose, a Council School ; and I sat cheek by jowl next all the ragamuffins of the village, and the cane was much in use. We resorted to many dodges to alleviate the sharp, stinging strokes and lashes : to rubbing one's palms with onions, and to stuffing brown paper down our breeches. All the same, I learnt a lot the hard way, which stood me in good stead later on.

Came the Grammar School, to which I had to take train each day to town and back again. A really fine school in all respects, but up to a certain age I never seemed to grasp the rudiments of grammar or arithmetic. I could never master such a simple sum as, 'If a herring and a half cost a penny and a half, how much would a dozen and a half cost ?' Or 'What is a preposition ?' I seemed to be a nit-wit on such matters, until suddenly one day I appeared to change overnight, and could fathom those intricacies of herrings, cisterns, triangles, logarithms and the like. As time went on I chanced to gain a certain amount of distinction at the school, though I always got minus marks for Latin! But still, as I did not blossom out as a doctor, it mattered little.

From the Grammar to the Technical College, where science predominated ; that, as well as mince and rice pudding at the college's domestic-science room, which was served up to us every day of every week of all the years I was there! Then onwards to London University. No grants, scholarships or bursaries in those days ; the country was not spending money on Education as today to the tune of nearly £1000 million a year—over three million pounds a day. Fantastic! Education! or as I have heard it termed today as being what you have left over when you subtract what you've forgotten from what you've learned!

Back home again I came, lecturing in the evenings at my former Technical College, the whiles I was an articled-pupil in a large private public-utility undertaking, which was to fit into my career when the five years (again the 'hard years') were finished.

Finished they were, and at an early age (in my very early twenties to be exact) I went abroad to fill an important post in Colombo, Ceylon—a country rich in history ; however, on my voyage out the First World War was let loose (1914)—with the notorious German battleship, the *Emden*, cruising and molesting shipping all over eastern routes—and no Europeans (holding key positions in the island) were allowed to leave ; and so the bland, inefficient manager whom I was to displace kept his cushy job five more years. I often keep telling myself I have been running five years late through life! Such is life though ; these things just so happen.

As soon as the war ended in 1919, changes took place at once, and I set about, in the earnestness of youthful energy, to pull things together ; the Company was nearly broke, as most of its profits in the good old easy days had been purloined by the three Europeans (who controlled a native labour force of about 400) in drinking, betting, owning race-horses, loose living and so forth. The books were properly 'cooked'. I had certainly dropped into something beyond belief, and really commenced working from scratch. It was all a sorry business, entirely different from what I had experienced in England. Those who during the 'palmy days' had been accepted into the highest society because they had money to burn (the Company's money of course!) were shipped off back to Blighty in no time.

I well remember the day I arrived fresh from home. It was a Saturday the boat dropped anchor ; and light-heartedly I stepped ashore, complete with cabin-trunk and two or three suit-cases ; embarking on a new adventure ; a new life, the like of which I am sure readers can well visualise.

There was no one to meet me, although they had been advised. Later I learnt the reason : they took strong exception to my coming out since they feared they were in for trouble at my hands with sweeping powers. I quite believe they were hoping the *Emden* would have torpedoed the boat on which I was travelling!

No one, as I have said, except a host of coloured 'boys' crowding around, laughing and grimacing at an obvious newcomer. To say I was bewildered is putting it mildly.

There were only two or three motor-cars in the island then ;

and those privately owned. I looked around at the landing-customs stage for a conveyance, but apart from rickshaws, there were only a few horse-drawn carriages—like our 'Victorias' or phaetons in the days of 1900—and known locally as 'gharrys'. I chartered one to take me to the works. The driver whipped up his horse, a thin, emaciated Arab animal with its bones sticking out, reminding me of a map of the main arterial roads of Britain that one comes across in today's A.A. handbooks!

After about two minutes, he suddenly drew up alongside a native *boutique* (shop) and went inside, and after a talk with his friend there, pointed to me. He came out, and I could see he was wanting money, so I gave him half a crown or so from my loose change, as I had no Ceylon money. In he went again for a drink of arrack (which I subsequently learnt was the raw distilled product obtained from the coconut-tree—a poisonous drink in all truth) and a stinking cheroot. On we sped ; well, sped was hardly the word ; we just jogged along, for doubtless the horse realised it had only a year or less to live. Finally, and it could not have been more than twenty minutes, we arrived lock, stock and barrel at the works gates, which the watcher duly opened ; and with great pomp and ceremony we drove in.

Still no one to welcome me (of course it was Saturday—a half-day, even in Ceylon!), and I, a young man thousands of miles from home. I felt very lonely and homesick. Getting out of the 'chariot' gingerly, for its wheels and springs seemed to be made of the thinnest of material, there was now the question of final payment. As to this, there was a great deal of gesticulations (with the old wrinkled native watchman joining in, doubtless wanting his commission also) and foreign yatter ; and again pulling out a handful of change, in which this time there was a loose English pound note fluttering, I thought the best thing—in all innocence—was to let the driver sort it out for himself, and take what was the legitimate fare. Little did I know the Eastern mind or race! He took the English £1 note, salaamed to the ground and gave thanks to Allah ; and I went inside the office and to the bungalow above the main building which was to be my quarters as arranged.

I was afterwards told the fare from the jetty to the works was but three rupees ; or 4s. 6d. I had parted with £1 as well as the few shillings more at the outset. One learns by experience, 'One born every minute', I said, of a fool. I was truly one of the innocents abroad!

I often wondered what happened to my gharry friend and his horse ; it was the one and only time I sat in such a vehicle. Maybe he drank himself to death on his fortune that Saturday afternoon ; either that or bought himself a coconut-tree so he could get arrack *ad lib.*—and for nothing! And the horse ? Both will be in eternity now, for that was close on fifty years ago, and both were then well advanced in age!

So much for these beginnings.

I had many far-reaching changes to make, my London Board giving me their whole-hearted support all through the twenty-three years I was in Ceylon. The transformations made brought me much into the limelight, resulting in a great deal of consulting work in Hong Kong, Kowloon, Singapore, Shanghai, Bombay, Calcutta, Malta, Tangier and Gibraltar. Here the 'explorer' simile certainly came true : a variety of places in different tropical and semi-tropical countries, in which one had to deal with a heterogeneous mixture of races and castes. Each place had its own problems ; its own religious and political atmospheres ; above all, each had its own particular charm of women. It is said travel broadens the mind ; it also broadens one's views in respect of women's charm! No matter be they dusky Ceylonese, Greeks or of Scotch Highland blood, in truth we are all one people ; and Love can suddenly appear around any corner of the world. Even 'down-under'—at the other side of the world from us in Britain— the Maoris have 'AROHA-NUI'—lots of love.

When I first went abroad, I neither smoked nor drank. I was far too busy to think of anything but work ; to holding up the outposts of Empire! and to the building up of a bank balance, which I regarded as my best friend. I was even too preoccupied to think of, or look upon, the few English girls around ; let alone the very pretty native girls or the correspondingly beautiful Eurasians. The only mental relaxation was taking daily exercise after five o'clock in the realm of sport : golf, tennis and cricket. Without exercise one's liver became 'sluggish', and ill-health would creep in with a vengeance.

Heigh-ho! life was starting in earnest. And Love ? it was to come about suddenly towards the end of my Eastern career.

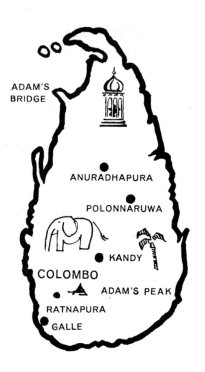

ADAM'S
BRIDGE

ANURADHAPURA

POLONNARUWA

KANDY

COLOMBO

ADAM'S PEAK

RATNAPURA

GALLE

CHAPTER 2

CEYLON

CEYLON, a country rich in history as I have just remarked ; and in the days when I was in the island, Britain was looked upon as a great Colonial power. Everything was pro-British. The British lion was well in evidence, right, left and centre ; and incidentally the word 'Sinhalese' means LION RACE, and their official flag to this day (which flies from my flag-pole at my Gairloch, Wester Ross, residence) bears on it an emblem of a great lion.

What a change of wind occurred on 4th February 1948 (long after I had retired) when Ceylon, a Crown Colony, gained her independence, and became a fully independent member of the British Commonwealth.

Ceylon, the sceptr'd isle—or, as I always termed it, 'The Isle of Delight'—hangs like a pear-drop from the chin of India only 70 miles away at its northern tip, known as Adam's Bridge, since

6

the two countries are almost connected by stepping-stone islets which legend tells us were built by an army of monkeys.

In tourist guides, Ceylon is spoken of in terms of an hospitable and charming people; famous tropic hotels; two separate climates, scenic beauty, wild life, ancient ruins, palm-fringed beaches, trout fishing and the like. An exotic life in all respects.

The island's recorded history begins with the landing in 544 B.C. of a North Indian Prince, Vijaya, and his 700 followers, on the north-west coast, who duly gained sway over the whole island. The Prince and his bands found their wives from India, from whence sprang the Sinhalese. They are therefore of Aryan descent.

The Sinhalese Royal line of 180 kings ruled Ceylon in unbroken succession for 2300 years, except for sporadic invasions by the Tamils of South India. They built magnificent palaces, halls and temples, great water tanks, and enormous well-shaped structures called 'dagobas'; some of them rivalling in size the Pyramids of Egypt.

With the advent of Buddhism in the 3rd century B.C., Sinhalese civilisation attained its fullest measure in the realm of engineering, art and sculpture—all inspired by a gentle faith. But only gaunt ruins of the once great cities can now be seen, relics of a bygone glory.

Ceylon's riches, ivory, pearls, gems, camphor, cinnamon and other spices attracted strangers from across the seas. The Portuguese in their caravels came in A.D. 1505, and left behind them strong Roman Catholic communities still in evidence today; and it is said there are more Portuguese names than there are in Portugal itself. The Dutch came next in 1640-1776, and introduced Protestantism. Their descendants, the 'Burghers' (of whom I will have more to say later on), were a hard-working, progressive people.

The British took over possession in 1776, and this 'Isle of Delight' flourished. It was during the brief, yet exciting, days of coffee planting (*circa* 1825), when Ceylon coffee found a ready market in the United Kingdom, that labour was first recruited from South India (Tamils) under the indenture system.

The coffee industry, from its slow beginnings, reached its peak in 1869. It helped develop vast enterprises such as banking and trade, transport and forwarding agencies. Thus did the pioneers see the bright days. But such prosperity did not last long. A fungus disease began to attack the coffee plant. It was first noticed in that year of 1869, and within a decade the whole industry had been blighted, and before the planters bestirred themselves from their complacency, the crash came. It demolished the very foundations of many a European company. The planter as well as the kangany (foreman) packed their bags— folded their tents in the night like the Arabs—and left.

But later on the planter, the kangany, the workers and their families returned to the scenes of desolation with renewed vigour. They laid out new fields to plant TEA ; and when the green of tea blanketed the land where the coffee tree had withered, there was hope again.

This widespread cultivation of tea, apart from rubber and coconuts (the cinnamon of Ceylon, famed in Biblical times, had been the lure drawing the island's European conquerors), required a large resident labour force ; and when the Sinhalese and the Kandyans were not willing to engage themselves in a work that was repugnant to them, the deficiency had to be supplied from India. Although there was a ban on emigration as early as 1847, India later lifted it in favour of Ceylon. The historical, cultural and religious ties that bound the two countries were thought to be sufficiently strong to ensure the protection of the immigrants.

These people had to trek hundreds of miles from various parts of South India to reach the coast, and thereafter were brought in primitive vessels (catamarans) to ports in Northern Ceylon. These veritable pioneers must surely have suffered much hardships, fevers and the like ; their tiny boats often being caught up in the monsoon winds and tossed around like toy boats. How their womenfolk and their plentiful number of children, as most of them had, stood up to it all is difficult to imagine. But they sang and chanted their way through marsh and jungle forest infested with wild life—leopards, jackals, rogue elephants, snakes, swarms of leeches, and hundreds of various obnoxious insects. Many would have perished on the pitiless trek. Walking scores of miles first through the dry zone then through the jungle, they reached the central hills, there to open up the plantations, the first task being the clearing of the jungle.

They were grouped in sub-gangs under family heads, and

those in turn formed a major gang with the Head Kangany as their chief. He was their philosopher and friend, their money-lender and shopkeeper. In short, the ordinary cooly worker found himself a virtual prisoner 'twixt this set-up of the Kangany and the 'Dorai' (the planter). A worker, male or female, had to step off the road when the 'master' came by on his rounds.

The acreages under cultivation of some of Ceylon's chief crops may be put as under :

Tea	572,000	acres
Rubber	658,000	,,
Coconuts	1,071,000	,,
Paddy (rice)	1,050,000	,,
Cocoa	50,000	,,

Amongst this green mountain fastness, the Dorais built their beautiful bungalows and clubs ; while the Head Kanganys erected temples for the worship of his workers. During the many festivals spread out through the year, the Dorai would go off hunting, whilst the workers celebrated with song and dance. Men, women and children gathered at the temple grounds ; and there, draped in their multi-coloured saris with flowers in their hair, and with betel's red on their lips, these tea-maidens would dance to the accompaniment of their anklets and the tom-toms. After their obeisances to the muse, they saluted the Head Kangany with the respect of that due to a feudal chief.

After such festivities it was back again to the regular routine in which trivial incidents in the field or factory, in their cooly lines (rows of huts) or at the water pump, rounded off the emo-tional lives of the workers.

The indenture system was abolished in the 1920's, whereupon the cooly and other workers could free themselves from 'debt' and could move about freely, seeking employment wherever they pleased.

Apart from produce, the British built roads, railways, schools and hospitals ; a certain amount of health service and naturally representative democracy, and established the first jury system in Asia—and the first women's suffrage. With the advent of self-government in February 1948, much 'bloody' reactions were against making Sinhalese the official language, downgrading English and Tamil ; but law or no law, English is still the current language, even in government offices.

B

I would mention it has been found there are some seventy different racial strains in Ceylon, mixing their blood streams freely. Afghans—fine six-foot upright frames—who appear to monopolise money-lending, extracting extortionate rates of interest once a poor native cooly falls into their clutches ; Moors (Arab-descended traders) who have cornered the lucrative gem trade, to say nothing of the Kuravar 'gipsies', who do all the snake charming! A few—a very few—Veddahs still survive, remnants of the island's original owners, now living deep in the overgrown jungle ; seldom seen, but relying on their bows and poisoned arrows—possibly the most primitive human beings on earth today.

The two big groups by far are the Sinhalese (mostly Buddhists) and the Tamils (mostly Hindus). The former, the North Indian invaders, came, as I have already said, some 2500 years ago. They were energetic builders, and marvellous remains of great cities and reservoirs they built can be seen to this day. The Sinhalese were superb hydraulic engineers ; some of their great artificial lakes being 30 or 40 miles in circumference. Foremost among these remains of buried cities are Anuradhapura (*Annarajah-purer*) and Polonnaruwa (*Pollar-na-rue-er*), to which I allude later. These names are as bad as Gaelic names, I am thinking!

Ceylon has a population of nine million people ; of which roughly 65 per cent are Buddhists, 20 per cent Hindus, 9 per cent Christians and the rest Muslims.

This, then, was the background of my life for twenty-three years ; 7000 miles away from England ; the Isle of Delight, an island lying between 6° and 9° north of the equator (at times I would think we *were* on the equator itself), with a humid atmosphere of an English greenhouse. A comparatively small island, 270 miles long by an average 100 miles wide.

Colombo, with a population of about 450,000, and over 200 years old, is the capital. Its name stems from an ancient Arab name *Kalambu* (*Lanka* is the old Sanskrit name for Ceylon, brought down twenty-five centuries ago by the Sinhalese from North India). It was here, in Colombo, my main work kept me, except for periodical visits to Kandy, where my Company had another large public-utility concern ; and it was at Kandy—the ancient capital—that Lord Louis Mountbatten had his headquarters of South-East Asia Command (SEAC) in the Second World War.

Colombo fascinates the visitor by its intriguing blend of old and new ; the East and the West. Sleek limousines flash past lumbering bullock-carts and ancient rickshaws ; gorgeous colourful sarongs and clothes of the East mingle with those of the West. It is one of the greatest ports east of Suez—the Charing Cross of the East. Many of its streets are flanked by flower-bearing trees : the jacaranda, gold mahur, royal poinciana—an unforgettable sight when in bloom. It is supposed to be the Garden City of Asia. It is also a city of temples and mosques. The minarets of the latter, the richly embellished façades of the Hindu temples and the murals of Buddhist temples, captivate the eye.

Up to 100 years ago, Colombo harbour was an open roadstead, and the town of insignificant size. Construction of an artificial harbour in 1878 and the opening of the Suez Canal led to the port's rapid growth. There is an English shopping area (the Fort) and a native shopping centre (the Pettah)—a typical Eastern bazaar.

Eight miles south of Colombo is the beautiful sea resort of Mount Lavinia; with safe sea-bathing; and at eventide, to see the incoming quaint fishing canoes (catamarans) beaching under the swaying coconut palms is a spectacle to linger in one's mind for all time.

Further down the coast, at the bottom end of Ceylon, is the ancient port of Galle, with a population of 56,000 ; Galle, the Tarshish of the Bible, to which Solomon sent his argosies for spices, ivory, peacocks and ebony for the Queen of Sheba.

Broad, golden and palm-fringed are the beaches of Ceylon, which match the dreamy, languorous beauty all around. Truly on Ceylon, nature has poured her gifts with a lavish hand ; scenic beauty, blue mountains, green valleys, silvery rippling streams, turquoise-blue waters breaking over coral reefs ; pretty and ever-smiling women, and a countryside that is as fresh and as Arcadian as when—according to legend—Alexander the Great visited it 2300 years ago. Along the countryside, one constantly passes emerald-green terraced paddy (rice) fields, over which shadows cast by the fierce tropical sun sweep each like a blush over a proud and sensitive face ; lush vegetation, thatch-roofed huts of coconut-palm leaves, village wells and bathing-places

where the local women flock to at noon ; a little *vihare*, or
temple, to which on full-moon days (*paya*) white-clad devotees
make their way to pay homage to the Lord Buddha ; and the
little *boutiques* (wayside shops) where the gossip of the village is
exchanged. All set midst a web of orchids, hibiscus and the
ever-present, ever-swaying coconut-trees; and of course of countless mosquitoes ! If you killed one, a hundred more turned up for
the funeral ; very similar to the midges of western Scotland !
(A good simple tip for midge bites is to rub the affected part
with washing soda, which relieves the sting and prevents swelling
on a sensitive skin.)

A countryside of relaxation and loveliness. As the great sage
wrote over 2000 years ago—'Yet a little sleep, a little slumber, a
little folding of the hands to sleep'—this typically depicts the life
and soul of the Ceylon villager.

It was here, then, in Ceylon, and in Colombo in particular,
towards the close of my twenty-three years' sojourn, that I fell
in love. In a country of flamboyant trees and a myriad of other
exotic flowering-plants ; and of the perpetual waving palms ;
an island rising up from the sea which opens magic casements to
every traveller ; in the tropics under a tropical sky, providing
unforgettable tropical moons!

> Give me the moonlight,
> Give me the girl . . .

was the song our chocolate-coloured coon singers used to head
the bills with in Music Halls of the 1900's ; the last line sung
crescendo with arms imploringly outstretched. A great song to
be sure ; nowadays it is more of the jazz and 'Twist' ; nothing
approaching the old days of 'Moonlight and Roses'.

This particular song became the signature tune of the native
Ceylon Cricket Association—of which I was an honorary member.

CHAPTER 3

CEYLON AND MARCELLE

IN a previous chapter I made the point of being so engrossed in my business career except in so far as sport was concerned ; and this was essential to fitness in such a 'muggy' climate. Moreover, it cleared one's brain ; it wiped away the cobwebs, and one felt greatly refreshed after coming back to one's bungalow, a hot bath and a good meal. Fortunately I was well served by a Tamil male cook who was with me for more years than I can remember, and who could always be relied upon to make a first-class meal even if I brought back two or three friends un-expectedly from the Club. Life in that respect was easy, and 'out of nowhere' would come something to whet our appetites. Everything was laid and served in immaculate style. The cook of my Ceylon days would put many a chef here to shame. He would never take a holiday, not even a day off. I think that was because if he did, his deputy would not record in my daily cannik book (the day's cost of food) the same buying price rates as he did ; and so the commission he got on every little article he bought in the bazaar—and which was not allowed me of course— might come under suspicion when he came back! He would never have admitted he took one cent of master's money—oh! never— ; and with innocence staring me out of his eyes, excitedly say he only charged me what he paid out in the market-place. I suppose each day he would 'make' about ten cents ; say one penny!

At the time I wish to relate, I played a great deal of cricket and was universally known as Bee Jay. Hence the pen-name of this and my other book on Wester Ross and Skye, *And It Came to Pass.* I suppose a double-barrelled name was too big a mouthful for all and sundry ; including the Police!

Being the President of the Mercantile Cricket Association, which controlled some forty-eight clubs in Colombo—drawn from the staffs (mostly native) of the Mercantile (*i.e.* professional) stores and firms—I always joined in these affairs. We divided them into three divisions according to their standards. Each vied with one another, and the winning teams were suitably inscribed on large silver shields which the particular firm held for one year. And then the same arrangement and 'feuds' started all over again. It was great sport, and much talent was displayed.

I used to be quite handy at knocking up half-centuries, and at times notching a century ; by then I was wet through and tired, and throwing everything to abandon, was generally bowled out when I had scored 101 runs!

Many of the players brought their wives, daughters and sisters to watch the great displays from the pavilion ; and on quite a few occasions I noticed, on coming in from the field, an especially pretty little dusky girl seated, along with others, in the front row. But she did not appear to be interested, save in the game.

I asked one of my team-mates one Saturday afternoon who she was, and was told she was the daughter of an old-established Dutch-Burgher family—one of many sisters—and she worked in the office of a native firm of booksellers in Colombo. No more, no less ; and whilst I appreciated the colouring—the beautiful colouring of dresses, saris and the like, scintillating on the many sunny afternoons in cricketing surroundings in the tropics—I really paid no more than passing attention. I noticed she clapped enthusiastically when I returned to the pavilion after making a goodly score. She did not seem to mind which side won!

In these latter days of my working in Colombo I rented a bungalow up in the hills, some four or five hours' run from Colombo, at a place called Bandarawela (*Band-dar-a-wellah*), near Diyatalawa (*Dee-at-a-lava*), which peaceful health-resort the British, as far back as 1900, developed from a few tiny huts into a convalescent camp for our soldiers during the Boer war ; and in its wake as time passed, many Europeans built bungalows for letting.

Bandarawela, having a dry, invigorating climate—the island's best-known sanatorium—was about 4000 feet above sea level ; not too hot ; not too cold, and it was a real refreshing treat to motor up there from steamy Colombo for an odd long week-end.

It served as a tonic, and a break ; for business was growing fast and profits seemed to know no bounds ; and of course with all that came extra worry, extra responsibilities.

Apart from the Company's car, used only for business, I had my own car and driver, which enabled me to often take advantage of such breaks ; I would sit back in the car and relax, allowing my native driver full control on the journey up to the hills and rounding the twenty or thirty *real* hair-raising 'hairpin bends' ; and as he seemed to have an enormous big toe (natives never wear shoes, of course, and rarely sandals), the latter came in most handy for 'stepping on the gas'. Goodness knows what his life would have been, but for his big toe! However, we used to get there on the dot, and a meal ready and cooked by a neighbour's cook, who was only too happy to oblige and look after me those weekends, thereby adding a few extra rupees to his dowry.

In reaching Bandarawela we had to pass through semi-tropical KANDY, where I called in to see the works there and settle outstanding queries ; thence onwards 'to the hills', through wonderful country and jungle, rubber at first, then as the altitude rose, tea ; for rubber does not seem to grow above 2000 feet.

It was on one of these occasions, as we were but a few miles from Kandy, and everything going smoothly, the car behaving like a bird, when 'BANG!' and upon drawing the car to a halt from its unnatural wobble and getting out, found we had a burst tyre. It happened at the outskirts of a little village, and soon we were surrounded by a swarm of male villagers seemingly appearing from nowhere, all jabbering away, laughing and smiling, showing their red betel-stained teeth (as though they were all suffering with a perpetual hæmorrhage from the mouth, for they are habitual chewers of the betel-nut, the nut of the areca palm. They chew it with a touch of lime paste—like some men chew, and spit out, tobacco—and which is supposed to be a delicacy!), and looking upon our catastrophe as a joke, and one which did not frequently happen to a 'sahib' amongst their peaceful, palm-fringed huts. No one, of course, proffered any help, for the motor-car was a thing quite out of their world ; and as my driver had no material to effect repairs, and the spare tyre, I found, had been left behind by my forgetful, haphazard Jehu, the only solution was for him to take the tyre off to a Kandy repairer ; and so he jumped into a rickshaw belonging to one of the villagers, saying he would be back 'shortly'. And shortly in Ceylon could mean *narliki*—tomorrow!

I got out of the car to try and find some shade from the blazing sun, and walking along to the edge of the village, I espied the familiar wayside water-well, a common sight in all these villages ; where the women come to draw water for their cooking needs, carrying the copper urns or pitchers on their heads back home (mud huts we would term them), as in the Old Testament days. I felt I could do with a cool, refreshing drink.

As I drew near, I saw there were two or three women— youngish—standing around the well, not in native dress, as were the cooly-women (the 'drawers of water'), but in semi-gaily-coloured European attire, just chatting and apparently passing the time of day.

I stopped and asked if I might take a sip from the spring, and one of them offered me a metal cup to drink out of ; and whilst taking it and glancing more particularly at her, I suddenly drew back in blank astonishment, wondering if my eyes were deceiving me. 'Tell me,' I said, somewhat falteringly, 'have I not seen you before ?' 'Yes, I believe so,' she answered in faultless English and with exquisite grace and bearing, albeit looking demurely. 'In Colombo ?' 'Yes,' she said, 'I live in Colombo, and am sure it is you I so often watch at cricket.' That was it then ; and it all came back to me in a flash. Truth is stranger than fiction!

Getting more into conversation with her, as seemingly she did not object, I gathered her name was Marcelle ; that she was of Dutch-Burgher parentage, living with her aged mother in the Cinnamon Gardens district of Colombo. Her father, who had died some years previously, had had a fleet of horse-drawn landaus which were principally engaged in meeting the mail-boats to and from Europe, conveying passengers for an hour or so around Colombo. These were the days before the motor-car. He was also a trainer of race-horses. She had two sisters, and worked (as I well knew of course) with a small local bookselling firm in Colombo, but was not too happy there, for she so wanted to get into a European office to work, as she could type and had a fair knowledge of shorthand. 'How come,' I said, 'you should be here in this jungle-village of all places ?' She explained she was having a few weeks' holiday, staying with a cousin who was managing a tea-cum-rubber plantation, a mile distant ; that she had sauntered down to the village to meet a few local girl friends, collect a little fruit from the bazaar, and was going back up to the estate bungalow shortly.

She had very smooth, black hair, a well-shaped nose, rather prominent cheek-bones (as most Eurasian women have), a *café-au-lait* coloured skin, teeth like real ivory—shown up to advantage by her dark skin—large brown eyes, the colour of milk chocolate about to melt ; and a slim figure. In short, she looked like a Vogue model ; oval face, long lashes and nice lips ; the total 'ensemble' being far from cold and calculating. Long mani-cured fingers and moon-shaped nails ; and surrounding all, a disarming smile. She walked lithely and upright, just as all the oriental nymphs do, swaying her supple waist. In fact, I would quote the poet Byron (who was a cousin of the wife, Anne Beatrix Horton, of Sir Robert Wilmot Horton, at one time Gover-nor of Ceylon) as follows : 'She walks in beauty, like the night of cloudless climes and starry skies ; and all that's best of dark and bright meet in her aspect and her eyes'.

We looked eagerly at each other, and I felt I was looking into a joyous, open-hearted girl, whose speech was as honey and milk under her tongue ; and she would be about 28 or 30 years of age. A girl so very different from the ordinary European girl who came out to Colombo, and who—I found to my cost—wanted nothing but a good time every evening of every night of the week ; girls that hopped around like will-o'-the-wisps. 'Good-time Charlies', as their opposite sex would be called!

She said she was sorry we had had a misfortune with the car ; but I said my driver would soon be back, and we would then be on our way to Kandy, and thence up-country for the week-end. She indicated that if I had had the time, she would have gladly taken me up to her cousin's bungalow for coffee ; but I excused myself on grounds of work to do, and wanted to be up in the hills by tea-time.

The morning sun was brilliant, as it generally is in the clear Oriental sky, and it lit up her appearance to the full, throwing playful colours around her dress, and the whole setting reminded me so forcibly of the loveliest—and perhaps most perfect—story ever told ; namely that found in the Bible, in Genesis, chapter 24 ; the story of Rebecca at the Well, and of Abraham's servant in his quest for a bride for his master's son, Isaac ; and which dates back many thousands of years. A story in which we may see the love of God and the finger of God.

This time-honoured story, which never fades, nor does one ever tire of reading or of the telling of it, began with Abraham, who was old and well stricken in age, sitting in his tent at Hebron in the land of Canaan ; a venerable sage who had passed through many eventful years. His wife (Sarah), who shared in all his joys and sorrows, now lay in her grave in a cave of the field of Machpelah, before Mamre, and he knew that soon his time would come to lie beside her, when he would be 'gathered to his people'. At this stage he was concerned over the future of his well-beloved son who was unmarried ; and so he was anxious that Isaac should have someone (not a daughter of the Canaanites) worthy of his life and love, to be his companion and guide along the succeeding generations which were to be blessed—as had been his (Abraham's) lot. After much thought and prayer Abraham resolved to call his trusted servant, Eliezer, and to send him forth into the far country of Mesopotamia ; and there—so his prayers led him to believe—his servant would find one who was ready to share his son's life together with his great and everlasting heritage. And his servant was worthy of his hire.

He commenced the journey after taking with him priceless jewels and costly raiment from his master's rich storehouse ; with a song in his heart and a prayer on his lips ; with a cavalcade of camels and their riders moving silently across the desert, the brilliant stars showing them the way by night. In due course this quiet, prayerful band reached Haran, and the well just outside the city, at the time when 'women go out to draw water'. And at that moment the journey was destined to make history. The story continues as we know it today ; the Almighty had answered the prayers in wondrous fashion ; and the sure and invisible guiding angels had led the company in 'the right way'.

The servant gave the damsel, Rebecca (sometimes written as Rebekah)—who disclosed herself as being a near relative of Abraham's—a golden earring and two golden bracelets. The astonished damsel went to her home and told her family of the stranger who had asked her for a drink ; and later the whole band of voyagers sat down in her father's tent, where Eliezer told of his purpose in journeying so far afield ; and that he had no time to tarry. More jewels and raiment were bestowed on the girl to adorn her beauty further ; and gifts of gold given to her mother, and her brother Laban ; and thereafter came a joyful feast. All this to show that God's call was real, and there was no deception—tokens of an inheritance far greater than anything that Bethuel's household could boast ; and given with a liberal hand. One may visualise the delight and surprise of that family ; they would surely be deeply touched.

The next morning, however, a cloud appeared to descend upon the gathering, for both Rebecca's mother and brother said she must remain with them for 'a few days, at the least ten'. Certainly, they said, she would go later on, but not just at once ; not 'today' but 'tomorrow', a favourite Eastern trait in character. However, this crisis duly passed, for in 'calling the damsel and enquiring at her mouth', she, standing near those whom she loved and who had raised her up and who, too, loved her dearly— her answer to the question, 'Wilt thou go with this man ?' was the historic one, 'I will go'—a brief, irrevocable reply ; one which determined her happiness and her everlasting destiny. Whether she paused, faltered, blushed or hung her head in prayer, we are not told. Simply the three brief words 'I will go', falling from her lips like a sudden shot from a gun. Rebecca's decision was clear-cut and based on faith. She had never seen the wealthy prince in Hebron ; this servant might have exaggerated and told her a 'tall story' ; would she gain this prince's true and lasting affection ; why did the prince not come in person ; what of the bitter partings from her people and home ; what of the hazards of the journey ; and a hundred or so more questions and doubts she could have raised in her heart ? But she believed ; she had no unbelief.

She and her nurse Deborah and her maidservants then bade farewells to her people and all the retinue around ; and left with all their benedictions, never looking back. She started the long journey southward, along the fringe of the Syrian desert to her future home ; soon her former world was gone, and she found herself at the beginning of another.

Near the destination she sees a man labouring in the fields. The servant, recognising his master's son, tells Rebecca that this was her future husband ; they all dismount, and being the custom, she draws a veil, covering her face. Isaac instantly realises this is to be his beloved from the far country ; for he sees the jewels and

raiment she is wearing—his family jewels and robes. And at
that momentous meeting Love and History became sealed, written
and recorded down through eternity.

> She came before her King
> In robes with needle wrought ;
> Her fellow-virgins following.

In my case, however, I did not arrive with a cavalcade of
camels through the silent desert, but in a 20th-century motor-car ;
and I had not asked the damsel to let down her pitcher that I
might *drink* ; nor did she say, 'Drink, and I will give thy camels
drink also'—a sign of the character and disposition of the woman
worthy of a master's son. No ; I had merely asked to be allowed
a *sip* from the well. She was 'very fair to look upon', figuratively
speaking, as recorded in those olden days. I am sure, after enquiring who she was, and that *had* I been stranded, she would have asked
me to stay overnight at the plantation bungalow ; very akin to
'whose daughter art thou, and is there room in thy father's house
for us to lodge in ?' In later years, and since it was love at first
sight, I again reminded myself of the Rebecca of old and the
query, 'Wilt thou go with this man ?' and of the reply falling
from her lips, 'I will go'. In this Arabic retort there is a parallel
to the Gaelic phraseology ; for in English, posing the question
'Wilt thou go ?' we would simply answer, 'I will', for the verb
'go' is understood. But in the Gaelic, however (and seemingly
in Arabic), no such suppression as this occurs ; and one must
enunciate the whole verb, thus 'I will go'. Certainly this reply
is more pointed, more cryptic, than saying 'I will'.

Near by the well was an old wrinkled native potter, moulding
his wet clay with all the dexterity of skill these ancients have of
bygone ages. As I watched him, I thought of Omar Khayyám—

> For in the Market-place, one Dusk of Day
> I watch'd the Potter thumping his wet Clay :
> And with its all obliterated Tongue
> It murmur'd—'Gently, Brother, gently pray!'

I verily think a prayer *had* escaped from my lips.

Within the space of an hour or so, my driver returned and
fixed the tyre. Reluctantly I left the well, and Marcelle, saying I
might find opportunity of giving her a small job in the office of

our Kandy branch ; I took note of her address, and she said how lovely that would be, for she wanted to be away from Colombo's sticky heat, and it would be within easy reach of her cousin's estate to journey to and fro each day.

I left it at that, and I suppose she thought that would be the last she would see—or hear—of me. Also, for in her station of life and being of different blood, different colour, she could not hope for anything further. However, although she was dark, I thought of the Song of Songs which is Solomon, namely, 'I did not look askance because of her colour, since the sun hath looked upon me'.

As we drove on to Kandy, I kept thinking and thinking. Could this be the beginning of the Rainbow ? I knew I had about another four or five years before me in my work, until I was sufficiently secure in material goods to retire at an early age from the heat and burden of the day ; and to that end I was striving ; but I realised that nothing could come of this 'affair' whilst I was in Ceylon, as my Directors in London would never have allowed me to 'lower ?' myself in such an entanglement. It would needs be after I had retired from public life and had left for England ; then and then only no one could voice anything against such a marriage contract—if it should ever come to such.

I found at Kandy that my manager there *was* in need of an office girl, and I said I might be able to select the right person for him when I returned to Colombo. I was pretty certain in my mind I would!

We continued our journey that afternoon up on to the hills, passing through timeless valleys of apple-green paddy-fields, cows and oxen ploughing and drawing carts, all as of old. Tea and yet more tea, acres and acres of it, with marvellous vistas on all sides.

TEA is practically Ceylon's life-blood. They call it *Mahabadde* (Great Industry) and millions of pounds are exported annually. The best tea grows up-country, *i.e.* between 5000 and 6000 feet above sea level. The small tea bushes are painstakingly tended, pruned, irrigated and so forth. The Ceylon bush is related to the camellia and would grow 30 feet high if it were not kept pruned to about 4 feet. Tamil women mostly pick the 'flush'— the tender new shoots—once every ten days, tossing it into big wicker baskets slung on their backs. About 3000 shoots make but 1 lb. of finished tea. The picked leaves, taken each evening to the factory, are weighed (the worker receiving so much per pound of raw leaf), then withered, rolled, fermented and fired (at around 200° F. temperature for about half an hour) through a furnace carrying an 'endless belt' on which the leaves are spread. When packed ready for export, it will keep for years if hermetically sealed and properly stored. Other plantation industries are, as I have said earlier, rubber, coconuts, cinnamon and other spices, and to a lesser extent cocoa.

I spent the week-end lolling about, but always my mind came back to Rebecca at the Well.

Early on the Monday, my driver had the car ready, and we set off on the return journey to Colombo, to work, and to the heat. On the way through Kandy we drove up to the cousin's bungalow, chancing to find if Marcelle was around. She welcomed me on the parapet steps as we drew up, and I could not fail to notice a certain tremor in her talk, which, however, soon dissolved over tea and cakes. Before her cousin could bombard me with queries, I mentioned the fact that if she liked she could start at our Kandy office the following week ; that our European manager would give her every assistance he could in our specialised work, and that no doubt she could brush up her shorthand more, and, if so, prove really useful. And who knows, I said (and I said this with more than a casual degree of emphasis), after a while, and if she felt she wanted to return to Colombo, I might find her work of a congenial nature in my own private office.

I could see her eyes lit up at this remark ; and they both thanked me profusely ; she perhaps more so than her cousin.

I left after an hour or so, saying I wished her luck and that I would be hearing from the Kandy office as to how she was getting along.

As we sped down the narrow tortuous tea-plantation roadway both she and her cousin Eric were waving ; he in perhaps a desultory fashion ; she certainly with an earnestness of foreboding love. As we descended the many hair-pin bends coming to the main road, they faded out of sight, and my driver's big toe 'applied the gas!'

Busy in Colombo as per usual I confess I put the week-end's episode aside ; but only for a while, when I found myself reading

Genesis, chapter 24 again. The sheer literary grace of that story is, of course, all unconscious, for as its quiet drama unfolds, one's emotions are somehow or other touched at one's deepest level, for it is a story bringing us into touch with the quiet pastoral world of centuries ago. And in a Ceylon village, Time, too, seems to stand still, making it more realistic than ever of ancient life ; and I need no pen for apologising in giving the simile its spiritual meaning and elevation ; for is not love of a four-dimensional nature in its height, depth, length and breadth ? It is, as it were, an ocean without a shore to its fathomless depth. Rebecca's decision was based entirely on faith, and I kept wondering of my own faith ; as to whether my former world was to be changed, and that I would find myself on the threshold of another ; undreamed of, and unbelievable ?

My usual visits to Kandy took on an added pleasure, and each time I saw Marcelle there—making steady progress in the work— our mutual attraction developed.

After some six months or so, she told me she was homesick for her mother and Colombo, and I suggested she should therefore join our staff in Colombo, to which she readily agreed ; and in due course she was installed with one of the team of typists we had there. Her anxiety to please and to progress evidenced itself noticeably, and within a year she became my confidential secretary. And no one could have wished for any better secretary.

She knew all the confidences involved in a big business ; and I trusted her implicitly, never once finding my trust misplaced.

As I have implied before, it was 'not the thing' to mix with or make close friends of the natives, no matter whether they were Eurasians (the issue of a European marrying a coloured woman), Dutch Burghers, Sinhalese or what-not ; and such people were barred from belonging to the European clubs. There was a distinct social line even amongst the Europeans themselves. Those who worked in the shops and big stores had their own clubs, for they were 'shop-keepers', or 'shop-wallahs', and not supposed— or allowed—to mix in any social way whatsoever with those Europeans in the professional line of business—known as the Mercantile community. I was one of the latter ; the sahibs, so to speak, who were running the colony!

Accordingly, only at odd times, did I call and pay my respects to Marcelle's mother and the family at their charming little bungalow. They were always delighted to see me, and I always left feeling they had been honoured in my venturing into their abode ; and into their family circle.

There was one thing I thoroughly enjoyed when having a meal at Marcelle's home—a curry, made by their Tamil cook. Not just a curry as one gets in this country, even at any so-called Ceylon or Chinese restaurant in towns, let alone at some hotels. For none of them have the faintest idea of making a real hot, tasty curry with all its 101 trimmings. For one thing, they cannot do the rice properly ; it is generally soggy and messy ; in the East the cooks have a way of their own, and each grain of rice, when cooked, comes out as a separate grain from the other ; all dry, and it falls on one's plate like a cascade of hailstones in its whiteness. The so-called 'curry-powder' is but tepid and insipid in its heat and flavour compared to a curry dished up in Ceylon, India or Burmah ; the red-hot chillies (pods or fruit of the original Guinea pepper), the coconut freshly pulled from the tree in the compound outside and sliced like shavings from a joiner's bench ; the coconut milk and the rest of the ingredients—all highly flavoured and pungent, containing turmeric, ginger, cayenne, and a host of other 'secret' concoctions thrown in, known only to our friend, the Tamil cook—made up 'A curry' with a capital A. Heaped on to one's plate, and eaten with a spoon and fork ; with a glass of cold water, or cold lager, beside you ; and a large serviette to stop the beads of perspiration dropping on to the curry, and so diluting the famous dish! That is a curry, a real curry, passing all understanding.

Here is the secret of making the rice nice and flowery, each grain tumbling out independent of the other ; and not the usual soggy nature :

You need Patna rice—or long-grain rice, and to wash it *many* times in cold water to take away any dirt or dust clinging to the grains. Then, to 1 lb. rice add 2½ cupfuls of water in a pan and bring to the boil ; then lower the flame, or heat, and cook *very* gently, stirring occasionally, and cook until all the water is absorbed. You then have, when slightly dried off, rice cascading —each grain separate—like snow-drops.

As readers may gather, our friendship grew, and it was evident such friendship was mutually shared and went beyond the realms of platonic friendship. In point of fact I have never believed in any such thing as 'platonic friendship'.

At various week-ends it was arranged I would take Marcelle and one or other of her sisters up to the Kandy cousin (for it was never permissible to journey alone—the two of us), and it was always a refreshing change, and a real treat. Whilst there, and removed from the capital's strait-lacing attitude, we two would often go in to Kandy for a meal at the big hotel, and stroll around the lake, watching the tiny fireflies in their millions darting amongst the flamboyant trees at dusk. It was cool, quiet, peaceful; and all was well with the world—our world.

She told me of lots of ancient customs ; that the Tamils and the Sinhalese seemed to agree on only one thing, and that was astrology and horoscopes ('Lord Luck', or 'what the stars fore-tell', as we find it today in our national newspapers). Neither of that race, she said, would do anything of importance without consulting the oracles. Even a marriage date was ruled by an astrologer as to same being the auspicious date and hour. A marriage date ? The phrase, and the intonation she gave those three words, seemed to strike a chord in my heart.

It set my mind a-wondering.

CHAPTER 4

KANDY

KANDY, the last stronghold of the Sinhalese kings, retained its independence when the island's coastal belt fell to the Portuguese and Dutch ; but eventually yielded to the British in 1815. Here a proud nation came under the conqueror's heel, and every hill, defile and ridge tells a story of an epic fight for that most cherished of all possessions—freedom.

It is Ceylon's legendary upland beauty spot, 1600 feet up in the hills, and 72 miles from Colombo. It nestles with mellowness in a valley surrounded by Ceylon's longest river, the Mahaweliganya ; and in its heart is a beautiful lake with crenellated bund walls. It is an artificial lake, built by the last king of Kandy.

Kandy, with a population of 58,000, is the spiritual home of Buddhists the world over. On a beautiful site beside the lake is the Temple of the Tooth, enshrining a tooth relic of the Buddha, and is Buddha's most hallowed shrine. Although by western standards the particular molar is far too big to have been a human tooth, yet it literally draws millions of pilgrims from thousands of miles ; and in its honour Kandy gives the island's most colourful and greatest pageant each August—known as the *Esala Perahera*. The festival, the most spectacular in Asia, is held at night by the light of flaming torches, and lasts about ten days. On the final day the pageant takes place in the daytime. This Kandy Perahera is in the form of a procession consisting of drummers (tom-toms), exotic dancing by the far-famed Kandyan dancers (males), whip crackers, and as many as a hundred caparisoned elephants ; temple chiefs in all their oriental regalia, torch-bearers and so forth. A magnificent tusker, gorgeously bedecked and jewelled, bears on its back a jewelled casket used for enshrining the Sacred Relic of the Lord Buddha. The enormous crowds continually shout and chant their reverent 'sadhus'.

Marcelle and I used to watch this Perahera and all the 'fun of the fair' from the balcony of the main hotel. But not for long, as the deafening noise, the dust raised, and the nauseating smell caused by the coconut-oil flare-lamps, coupled with that of the huge mass of natives, got into one's nose and throat ; and we would leave in the early evening for the plantation—clear, pure air—whilst the festival would extend (like a Scottish Highland island wedding) to all hours of the morning, and repeat itself the next day and the day after that!

The ceremonial dances of Ceylon draw their inspiration from local mythology. Kandyan dancing is one of the most ancient art forms in existence. It is one of the most complex in its technique and symbolism, and still remains one of the purest forms of national expression in Ceylon—despite a century and a half of foreign contact. It is a people's art ; its movements are graceful and sinuous, and appeal to the aesthetic sense of exponents of traditional dancing the world over.

As usual, Marcelle would explain all the ceremony involved, and all its accompanying rituals and meanings ; never lost for a word or a sentence ; and to me, everything was of the utmost interest. Oriental splendour at its peak, mystifying and totally a world apart from our English understanding ; Eastern drama unfolding itself in a riot of colour, majesty and awe. And a little Eastern girl as a guide! with all the fascinating allurements Eastern women possess.

There are other temples of note : all beautifully executed in true Eastern architecture.

Four miles north of Kandy is Katugastota, the renowned bathing-place for elephants. The same distance south is the University of Ceylon, said to be the most magnificently sited university in the world.

Kandy is renowned for its work in lac, Kandyan silver, mat-weaving and tortoise-shell work. Copper, brass, ivory and ebony are also wrought by skilled craftsmen, using technique half as old as Time itself. These various arts—like the Kandyan dances—have been handed down from father to son.

The lacquer work is particularly pleasing in all its gay colourings ; and consists of ornamenting woodwork with the resinous secretion of the lac insect.

The great war-time film, *The Bridge on the River Kwai*, based upon that Japanese operation and heavy toll of prisoners of war, was 'shot' entirely in Ceylon ; many of the scenes were made in Kandy itself. In 1959 this was awarded the best British picture of the year. Another grand film, *Elephant Walk*, was also 'shot' in Ceylon ; as well as *The Purple Plain*, with Gregory Peck and Win Min Than.

There was truly much to see and do in and around Kandy each time we went there ; and much to think about. Many strange customs, and peculiar manners of speech.

À propos of nothing in particular, but very typically 'Ceylonese', I find it hard to refrain from relating the following story in the way in which a Ceylonese youth speaks in his somewhat high-tone voice in pidgin-English, which I am sure will amuse anyone who may have been in Ceylon. This youth went into one of the European stores in Colombo, wanting a gramophone record. 'What's the number of it?' enquired the assistant. "I say, man, look you here ; I do not know the number, man," he replied. 'Well, what is it called ; what is the title ; who is it by?' he was asked. Again he said, 'I say, man, I do not know exactly, man, but it was a record of such a size (indicating a 10-inch record) ; and look you, I think it was called "At 3 o'clock in the morning" on the front side, and "Who's kissing my sweetheart now", on the back side'!

CHAPTER 5

ADAM'S PEAK AND BURIED CITIES

ANOTHER time, for a change out of Colombo, we would go south-east some 20 miles to Ratnapura (*Rat-na-poorer*), meaning the 'City of Gems', and watch the native workers washing down gravel, dug from pits. They would stand knee-deep in a small stream, swishing shallow bowl-shaped wicker baskets, washing away the mud and sand. Exactly like 'panning gold' in the Klondike days ; the gems, being heavier, sink to the bottom of the basket.

From Ratnapura come the fabulous gems that have for the last 3000 years filled the treasure-vaults of sultans and shahs, and decked the crowns of kings and emperors.

Sheba's queen at the height of her glory drew her jewels from Ceylon ; King Solomon's argosies made hazardous journeys in quest of them.

Zircons, amethysts, moonstones, sapphires, tourmalines, rubies! Surely music in these names have poured in glittering cascades of a million hues into all the capitals of the world. Zircons and sapphires are often found a few feet below the surface. It may not be known generally, but the world's largest blue-star sapphire was bought in Ceylon by the financier J. Pierpont Morgan, and that sapphires and rubies are exactly the same stone except for colour. Yes, Ceylon produces practically all known gems save emeralds and diamonds. Certainly I thought during all our many times together, Ceylon *had* produced a real gem in Marcelle.

The change from the crude stone to the sparkling jewel is the work of the skilled lapidaries of Ceylon's City of Gems—Ratnapura. Using an age-old technique, they patiently and tirelessly bring to the surface the latent star in the blue sapphire, and the fire that glows in her heart. Hidden in the alluvial soil of Ratnapura is treasure beyond compare. Miners frenziedly search ; some draw blanks ; others, stones worth a king's ransom.

From Ratnapura one is not far from Adam's Peak : an odd sharp-coned mountain seen from nearly all parts of southern Ceylon. Its height, 7360 feet.

Marcelle recounted the many legends as we journeyed together.

After Adam and Eve were cast out of heaven—so says Moslem tradition—they had the choice of all the world's loveliest places for their earthly Garden of Eden ; and chose Ceylon. Adam's Peak is literally the holiest mountain in the world, revered by countless millions of people because of the foot-shaped impression in the rock at its top. To hundreds of millions of Moslems and Chinese this is held to be Adam's footprint. Then again, to 400 million Buddhists, the print is said to have been made by Buddha on his last visit to Ceylon. As to Hindus, they claim it to be the footprint of their god, Siva. So we have a number of theories!

There are many paths to the summit, but of course we never attempted the climb. On one dangerous, precipitous path you can only ascend by putting your feet into links of stout iron chain, supposedly put there by Alexander the Great ; yet another theory ; but the paths generally used by the ant-like hordes of pilgrims have thousands of steps cut into them. Mostly one commences the climb just after midnight, so as to reach the top for sunrise, and see the enormous shadow 'of a man's hand' cast by the peak. An eerie sight that fills one's soul with wonderment.

At the top, Buddhist priests, in their saffron-coloured robes, officiate at a tiny temple—one of Buddhism's proudest titles, 'High Priest of the Peak'. The Holy Footprint, the Sri Pada, is about five feet long and three feet wide.

Not far from Adam's Peak is Ceylon's highest table-land, Horton Plains, 7000 feet high. The view from 'World's End', where the plateau abruptly drops a sheer 5000 feet, is one of the most wonderful spectacles in the world.

So much for Adam's Peak ; so much for legends. I was learning a lot of Ceylon folk : their habits, their history ; their religious ramifications. Marcelle was always helpful, and had a fund of information ; and love seemed to take on a different meaning as we stood at the bar of so many beliefs. I am sure she was saying to herself, if I had asked her *then*, 'I will go'.

Another tour we made was to Anuradhapura and Polonnaruwa

—two places mentioned earlier; how we enjoyed this visit 'Down the Corridors of Time', as I called it. Anuradhapura is 150 miles north of Colombo and was founded in 437 B.C., when the Parthenon of Athens was being built. It had a population of three millions, ranking with Babylon and Nineveh; and for one thousand years was one of the world's greatest Buddhist cities. Now, it is a mass of crumbling ruins and hoary monuments— remnants of a glittering city. (Polonnaruwa, about 60 miles south-eastwards, is some 1700 years younger; and both cities ultimately declined with collapse of political struggles, and were lost for centuries.)

In its heyday, Anuradhapura was larger than London, and it lasted longer than either Rome or Carthage, or mighty Thebes. The jungle tide then crept over both these Ceylon cities, slowly overwhelming the palaces and statues; the monasteries and courtyards.

Today you may see the 1600 monoliths that once supported the famous Brazen Palace, an edifice nine storeys high with 1000 rooms finished in silver and studded with gems, and roofed with bronze and brass; together with a great hall supported by golden pillars as well as a huge throne of solid ivory for the high priest.

The colossal Dagobas (enormous dome-shaped temples) are amongst the greatest structures ever built of brick. The tallest, higher than St. Paul's Cathedral, had a platform supported by four hundred brick elephants, each one different, and each equipped with solid ivory tusks.

All this in 437 B.C.—just on 2400 years ago. Amazing is but a mild adjective to employ in all these matters.

The bricks in the largest Dagoba would suffice to build a wall 10 feet high and 1 foot wide stretching from London to Edinburgh. The sacred Bo-tree—the oldest authenticated tree in the world—still draws veneration from thousands of pilgrims. These temples all stand to the glory that was Anuradhapura, that for one thousand years was the capital of Ceylon. The Bo-tree just named is reputed to be a branch of the tree from Buddha-gaya, India, under which the Buddha attained enlightenment.

After Anuradhapura fell and was abandoned the Sinhalese —who were apparently better architects than fighters—built a second capital at Polonnaruwa, 60 miles away, as I have stated.

I have toured the ruins of Pompeii, near Naples, but never so impressed with the past as I was midst the ruins of Ceylon.

Polonnaruwa attained under Para Krama Bahu I, who was one of the greatest Sinhalese kings, a splendour and magnificence equalled by very few other cities of medieval times. It was regarded as a most dazzling capital. One of its most striking features is a gigantic image of Buddha ; alas now headless through the ravages of Time. Another impressive sight is a group of statues ; especially of two huge figures ; the standing one with folded arms, thought to be that of Ananda, the beloved disciple, grieving over the death of his master, the Lord Buddha. Never before—or since—has there been depicted in stone such poignant grief on the features of one ; and such absolute serenity on the face of the other.

Near to Polonnaruwa, in the heart of Ceylon, looms a giant boulder known as Sigiri Rock. It rises 600 feet above the sea of foliage washing round its base ; seen from a distance, as it humps above the trees, it looks like some huge animal in repose.

When King Kassapa I came to the throne by subterfuge and murder, he decided to leave his great capital city, Anuradhapura, taking up residence on the summit of Sigiri, building an elaborate palace on the three-acre ground. Much of the upper portion of the rock overhangs. After eighteen years there, his brother laid siege and ultimately Kassapa committed suicide. The fortress was abandoned and slowly fell into ruins.

'Sigiri' is a corruption of two words, meaning 'lion rock'. The entrance to the upper fortress lay between the paws of a colossal crouching lion, which must have dominated the landscape for miles around. Near the base of the western face of the rock is a great wall of glass-smooth yellow plaster—named the Mirror Wall ; much of which is in a perfect state of preservation even today. Need I remind readers that all this work was one thousand years before Columbus sailed for the New World ?

Beneath the overhang are the imperishable 'Frescoes of Sigiriya' : life-size paintings by an unknown artist, of elaborately jewelled and full-bosomed women, glowing with warmth and colour, emerging from a sea of clouds. The light of half a million sunsets has poured on these frescoes ; the wind and rain of fifteen centuries have beaten them, yet their reds and greens and yellows still appear bright from the hand of the master who created them ; *mirabile dictu.*

Marcelle and I saw all these wondrous, timeless, ageless works of art and culture together, spellbound. I listened to her telling me of all these buried cities ; all the legends ; all the intrigues ; all the loves of 2500 years ago. It was unbelievable that so much could have been wrought by 'natives' so long ago with just ordinary rough-and-ready tools. It was a revelation ; and in reverence and humility we bowed, paying homage, if not to a lost race, certainly to a lost kingdom. *Sic transit gloria.*

It is interesting to record that the oldest book in the world is a 16-foot-long Buddhist scroll, to be seen in the British Museum.

CHAPTER 6

THE FLEETING YEARS

THERE are many little wayside rest-houses (tiny hostels of a kind sponsored by the Government)—now known as 'Tourist Inns' since 1948 independence. The term 'rest-house' is derived from the Dutch 'rest huys' : a place of rest for the weary or benighted traveller, and where you call in for a meal and are allowed to stay one night only.

Nearly 150 years have elapsed since the first rest-house was built ; then it was just a little two-roomed house, gloomy, forbidding, bare, with a few rickety chairs, a makeshift table and two incomplete beds. Quite a change today (and in my time), where there is a network of these rest-houses (over 100) covering most of the island. In appearance they do not differ from the plain, stout buildings that the Dutch built during their period of occupation, from 1640 onwards ; it is only in their situation that discernment, even genius, has been displayed. The charge at these rest-houses is nominal, about 15s. for evening meal, bed and breakfast.

They mostly border on the seashore.

One of our particular beauty-haunts was Bentota (*Ben Tot*), which had just two bedrooms, and a Tamil cook who could put on a wonderful evening meal though caught out unexpectedly. Usually, mulligatawny soup, seer fish (caught whilst you were there!), curried chicken—hot, very hot—with all the trimmings, and jaggery pudding : a sort of hot sago mould made in thick, sweet, luscious 'jaggery' resembling the dark treacle one sometimes gets in this country. After a bathe in the ever-warm clear-blue sea lapping on the coral shore, one did real justice to such a banquet. And afterwards lying on 'long-sleever' deck-chairs on the verandah, with not a soul around, and not a sound to be heard except the innumerable crickets, madly chirping away ; with the moon appearing through the oddly-shaped coconut-palm trees, I would turn to Marcelle and say, 'Well, if Heaven is anything like this, then it *will* be Heaven' . . . a palm-fringed, sun-drenched island, pounding white surf, and the music of the blue, blue sea!

Then there was another charming resort we visited 'over the rainbow'—the hill station, 6250 feet above sea level, called Nuwara Eliya (*new-rail-ia*), with climate and scenery akin to Scotland's Wester Ross—minus the lochs—a startling paradox in the tropics. Its name signifies 'City of Light', and it is a town free of the din of traffic. It was only discovered as late as 1819 by the brother of the famous inventor Sir Humphry Davy. It has a golf-course, said to be the finest out East, and a picturesque race-course. Above all, it has the flowers of spring—phlox, gladioli, roses and chrysanthemums ; sweet peas, carnations, daffodils and scarlet rhododendrons, in bloom.

Marcelle was not allowed over the golf-course, for it was a 'European' course ; but at the races, all and sundry were there ; and what a kaleidoscopic panorama it was ! the latest creations in Western dress mingling freely with the endless beautiful colours of Eastern and native attire. 'Technicolor' at its highest, our film producers would term it ; sparkling in the extreme, drawing one's attention at times from the horses, which one had come to make money on, but more often than not, one's last-minute 'certainties' turned out failures at the winning post ! Enjoyment, peace and relaxation 6000 feet up in the skies, with a pretty Dutch Burgher damsel as companion.

The sweetness of flowers ; the rush of streams ; the rapture of love, and the peace of the hills were all there at our finger-tips—a tropical island with the world's holiest mountain towering nearly 8000 feet upwards from its green paddy-field base. Could one ask for more ? No.

The years sped on ; and becoming more and more attached, the question of our marrying arose ; for within another year I would be leaving Ceylon, having completed twenty-three years there, which I thought was enough, as I felt I would rather retire on the crest of the wave and enjoy such retirement whilst comparatively young. Her star-like eyes lit up with even greater appeal ; but she hinted 'Wouldn't there be difficulties in our way since we are,' she said, 'of two different, widely different, nationalities ; two different colours. Wouldn't people in England look askance at me married to a white man ?' . . . and so on. Whilst

I used to say there should be no misgivings, she would reply,
'Yes, true, but I'm a woman, and would feel it more ; the side
glances, the frowns and up-lifted eyebrows, the asides made by
the public generally. They would tend to "pass us by on the
other side"?' And so it went on. She began to be perturbed
beyond measure. It was a great perplexity, this colour and racial
complex. Religion did not enter into it at all ; she did not con-
form to the Buddhist or any other similar faith ; she and her
family were members of the Baptist Church in Colombo. 'What
would her mother, her sisters and friends say?' she said. They
would say she would feel a stranger in a strange land, and tell her
it was a long, long way to England ; and here again was a parallel
with Rebecca. It would be unreasonable for her to have a full
grasp of all that was involved in her decision and calling. As yet,
she stood on the threshold of a life, the wonder of which she
could hardly envisage; from that moment her name would, as did
Rebecca's, take on the colour of immortality. By one action she
would be stepping forward into history ; her name, her life and
her faith. The long, long journey, if she took it—separated
from her blood relations—would indeed be alive with interest,
looking to the white cliffs of Dover, and her future home. Certainly in that scene, and in that hour of arrival in England, there
would be a sense of undying love ; but would that love, that
life so very, very different, sustain us both in the after years,
through the many trials that she foresaw, and which she felt
we would be called upon to endure? The European way of
life, Marcelle said, would be entirely different ; the deep lustre
of love might well become tarnished? She was very practical
through it all ; though like Rebecca she realised the privileges,
honours and blessings that would come her way ; she appreciated
the new relationship, the greater dignity and honour that was
being bestowed on the question, 'Wilt thou go with this man?'
Many reading these lines will probably share both the views
and the doubts which Marcelle had ; that the crux of the matter
was, Can people of a different race and colour be happily wedded?
It was a problem. Of course we all know 'Love is blind' ; that
love sees with its own eyes ; that it is not of much avail trying to
influence those who *are* in love, to think otherwise ; to think
again. Such is Life. There is the story of a young man, tall, dark
and handsome, falling in love with a girl who was utterly plain

and unattractive in the extreme. When asked how he could ever imagine himself being married to such a person, he simply said, 'Well, if you could see her with *my* eyes, then you'd love her.' One cannot always judge by outward appearances, whatever one's colour, nature or looks may be. Marcelle was most colourful, and her general ensemble most attractive—to me. I had known her for a few years, so it was not a case of a whirlwind romance, or sudden overt emotionalism ; neither was it a question of 'novelty'—a white sahib courting and sleeping with a coloured woman.

She generally felt there would be all-round opposition to our union ; and besides, she confided in me one night, there was a Ceylonese widower in his early forties, who was a great friend of the family, and they were all imagining something would come of it. It was true the family liked me very much indeed ; that she loved me tremendously—not him ; and that was absolutely true. In fact, she worshipped me, she said. After Xmas 1936 I could see she was getting nervy and losing a little of her concentrating aplomb. As I was booked to sail for England on 1st April 1937, I thought it perhaps a good idea if she took a break, and went up to her cousin's plantation for a month or so, before I left Ceylon's shores ; and to 'think on these things' amidst the environment of peace and beauty. She readily fell in with the suggestion ; she would write twice a week, and vowed she would see me before I sailed. In case of any eventualities—illness, or such-like coming our way, I gave her—as further faith— my Bank address in England, for at that time I had no idea where I would settle down to live. But she would come before I sailed ; and on that solemn assurance, she left for Kandy.

Her letters at first were full of love ; then they became full of what her cousin was doing and of life on the plantation. On my part, although I was hard-pressed in winding up affairs and initiating my successors into office (two Europeans came over from our Hong Kong branch to replace me), I wrote every week, often commenting on the Rebecca at the Well incident ; but I felt it prudent not to try to persuade her in her future life. There is no lasting love in either the one or the other in 'persuading'. For complete happiness, both must be in love ; both must merge into each other's life as one. It must be 100 per cent both ways, so my heart told me, and it still tells me that today. Then all is, and must be, well ; and not a living soul can shake such a combination. Mutual trust engenders mutual love, and *that* passeth all understanding.

The weeks moved on, and her weekly letters continued to arrive. She knew the day of my departure, and nothing would prevent her seeing me off.

In the interim, I continued to call at her mother's house ; and they welcomed me as of old. They all had quite an affection for me.

It was a Wednesday when the 30,000-ton Orient liner *Otranto* put into Colombo harbour. I had phoned 'Cousin' during the week-end to ask for Marcelle, only to learn she had gone back home the previous week. Strange, I thought, she should not have come along to the office, or seen me. However, I had a great deal to do, and a great deal to pack, and many farewell functions, but I felt certain she would come. Wednesday came, and still no news or sign. I sent a *peon* (office boy) round to her mother's home with a note. He came back saying 'missy not at home'.

Since we both had each other's address, I knew we would still be in touch, come what may. The boat was scheduled to sail at midnight, and I went aboard in a private launch about 9 p.m., after dining at the hotel. Many were there to bid me *bon voyage*, farewell and good luck ; many to say what was Ceylon's loss would be Britain's gain—and other flattering remarks.

About 11 o'clock, my business friends having left, I went down to my single-berth cabin, just to straighten out my baggage and tidy myself up, prior to going on deck at midnight to see Colombo's harbour lights fading out.

A knock at the cabin door. 'Come in,' and who should it be but Marcelle! My heart stood still, as my pulse missed a few beats. 'Marcelle,' I said ; and clasped her in my arms. She held away slightly, for she was carrying one dozen red, red roses. 'I've come as I promised, Stanley,' she said falteringly, 'and brought you these' ; and with that she turned on the cold water at the basin and put the flowers in. 'Darling,' I said, 'how wonderful to see you.'

She was dressed, as always befitted her, plainly yet exquisitely, in a shantung-silk pleated skirt, and a coatee ; wearing on the lapel the little brilliant I had given her a year ago ; white court shoes, fine silk stockings, white net gloves, and a scarf round her open neck.

She seemed in a hurry, for she said it was near midnight and she could hear the shouts of 'all visitors ashore' ; though I must confess I never heard anything, for I was 'out of this world'.

She looked as usual, very pretty, but her eyes lacked the sparkle and lustre of the days when we were at Bentota, Kandy, Adam's Peak and the many other places we knew so well.

Oblivious to time, and sailing orders, I said, 'Sit down, darling ; tell me your answer.' She was still nervy and quivering slightly, but I put that down to the suddenness of our meeting ; for in all such momentous episodes one is generally tongue-tied. We tried to form words unsuccessfully. Then after a few silent seconds she said, 'I've only a minute, Stanley,' and took off her left glove. 'I was married last week, dear.'

After a pause—a sickening pause—I said, 'To him ?' 'Yes,' she murmured, 'to him.' 'But you're not in love with him, Marcelle ?' 'No,' and breaking down, she sobbed in my arms like a child.

> The plain golden ring that she wore
> Was the last, through my tears, that I saw.
> The Isle that I called my Delight
> Was no more, as I sailed out of sight.

CHAPTER 7

AFLOAT AND AWAY

MIDNIGHT, and zero hour. The *Otranto* weighed anchor, and after glancing at the harbour bar through a tear-dimmed porthole, I flung myself on the bunk, never bothering to undress ; and I must have gone off to sleep at once through sheer mental exhaustion, for it was not until the steward brought in my early tea at 7 a.m. that I saw we were in mid-ocean. It was raining, but the sun was shining through, and a complete rainbow encircled the horizon.

A rainbow! on which I had put such hopes. Ceylon was now at its one end, and I wondered, as we travelled through the arc to the other end of life's rainbow, what would be in store ; for I could feel the creep of loneliness the while. By the Suez Canal and Egypt, we would be half-way through the arc ; and in England at the other end of its red-orange-yellow-green-blue-indigo-violet spectrum.

> *Que sera*, *sera*, whatever will be—will be.

> . . . The Moving Finger writes ; and, having writ
> Moves on. . . .

Whilst the almond-tree flourished, the grasshopper became a burden ; the pitcher at the fountain was broken ; as was the wheel at the cistern.

A rainbow! I mused. There was not a single word of the Scriptures written in Abraham's (Rebecca's) days. What it pleased the Lord to communicate to man, His Word from the first promise in the Garden of Eden till the days of Moses, 430 years later, had to be conveyed from father to son traditionally.

A rainbow! When He made a covenant with Noah about 440 years before Moses' time, He gave him a visible seal, namely the rainbow in the cloud. So till this day, the rainbow is the seal of the covenant of God made with Noah and with all flesh in whom there is the breath of life, that He would not again destroy the whole earth with a flood for the wickedness of man.

This bears testimony before our very eyes to this day ; and the faithfulness of the Lord to all His promises.

As the sands of Time then appeared to me as sinking, I was fortified by the rainbow, in that one day the dawn of Heaven *would* break. We learn many things best by contrast ; the rainbow is never seen so bright as in the bosom of a dark cloud ; also that the darkest thunder cloud only covers the heavens for a time.

The days on an ocean liner are, for the most part, care-free ; and sitting on a deck-chair with nothing but sea and 'emptiness' before me, I began—as I have said—to muse, and to straighten out the rough with the smooth. *Que sera, sera.*

I pictured to myself a number of vessels at different times and from different places bound for the same port. As regards the compass steered by, the port of destination, the general rules of navigation, astronomical readings taken daily and so forth—all would be identical. However, differences *would* occur. None of the vessels would encounter the same winds or weather. Some would have a goodly gale astern helping them along ; and when all was set fair, they might suddenly get a set-back by adverse currents ; but after enduring hardships, would emerge safely, and so reach harbour. Others, beset by storms at the beginning and driven off course, would finally run into calm seas, and they, too, would enter port safely. The remainder might well meet with no misfortunes at all, in their voyage through the seven seas.

Surely, I thought at this time, one's life was very like these vessels of human cargo ; human bondage. It was all a question of Life with a capital L ; in other words *Kismet*, an Arabic word for Fate, Destiny, or one's lot on earth.

As we passed through the Red Sea, with Arabia on one side and Egypt on the other, my mind turned to yet another story in Genesis : the story of Jacob's love for Rachel (Laban's youngest daughter) and of the fourteen years he waited. As I looked across Arabia, with my spirits at such a low ebb, I felt the River Euphrates was verily drying up. The red roses in my cabin had all drooped ; the living sap had flowed out of the stems.

I was bound for England ; the date April 1937.

During the early part of that summer I paid a prolonged visit to Gairloch, Wester Ross ; for all through my years abroad, whenever I came home on leave, every two and a half years, I invariably spent long months up in Gairloch searching for a site that I could build upon for my retired days, to be spent amongst the wonderful country there, and the wonderful people of Gairloch and district ; an enchanting land 'at the end of the rainbow that offers so much of everything to everybody at all times of the year' (vide *And It Came to Pass*).

Later that year I was asked to consult on works in Gibraltar and Tangier (across the straits in North Africa) ; and once again embarked eastwards. During that short voyage I chanced to meet on board a young lady and her father, who were travelling to Port Said to their home in Alexandria, Egypt. She was feeling very sea-sick ; Pater (as she called him) was recovering from a recent illness, and as I was somewhat below par in spirit, the three of us used to sit in the spacious lounge looking out on to the ocean ; for it was quite unthinkable to sit out on deck going through the Bay of Biscay in October.

It seemed Pater, Lancashire-born, was in the cotton trade in Egypt.

Her mother was a Greek.

She was an exceptionally nice girl, about 35 years of age ; extremely pretty, shapely and soignée, with dark hair, blue eyes and the face of a ravishing Greek beauty. All Grecians, as a rule, are pretty ; she was the prettiest I had ever met. Like Helen of Troy, she had 'a face that launched a thousand ships' ; the sort of girl you'd expect to meet at a fashionable cocktail party or a champagne supper ; veritably '*attrayante*' ; and *séduisante*, in the term 'bewitching'. Her name was Tháfne—pronounced as we would Daphne, though the 'th' is as 'vaff'—which is Greek for Laura. It is also the Greek for the laurel bush.

Greek mythology yields legend upon legend ; and there is a very touching one over this name and word Tháfne. The Sun God, Apollo, quarrelled with Cupid, the Love God, and to revenge himself, the latter shot one of his 'love'-pointed arrows into Apollo's heart ; at the same time shooting a 'hate'-pointed arrow into the heart of the beautiful nymph, Tháfne. When Apollo chanced to see Tháfne, he adored her—but she loathed him through Cupid's act of 'hate'. She ran away, but Apollo pursued her, until in despair she begged her father—the River God—to save her. The river heard her prayer and changed her into a laurel-tree (*thafne*). Apollo wept and decreed that for ever after his beloved Tháfne's leaves would crown the heads of victors ; and be green in winter and summer alike. So the Greek word for 'laurel' has been *thafne* ever since ; as has been laurel crowns for the mighty.

By the time we had reached Gibraltar, we had struck up a board-ship friendship of more than passing interest ; much more indeed. When I disembarked at 'The Rock', they both begged me to come and visit them in Alex. if I could. I said it was very nice of them to ask me, and that after I had finished my consulting work in Gib. and Tangier, I could quite easily make the journey and see them ; and Egypt too. One may say, you can't fall in love in so short a time as London–Gibraltar ; but you can, if the Fates decree ; *que sera, sera.*

I spent over two months in Gib. and across at Tangier.

Tangier, a city of excitement and adventure, was a veritable cosmopolitan place where one rubbed shoulders with the riff-raff of Europe : smugglers, cut-throats and the like—shifty characters, all. Ticket-of-leave men, and murderers escaping justice. My! what a place ; and to visit the Kasbah (native quarter) at nights, I usually had my friend the Chief of Police at my side.

It was most fascinating : Arabs in their flowing robes, French, Spanish, Bedouins (nomad Arabs), Greeks, Germans, Italians, Poles—and a sprinkling of English people also. No customs, no excise, no income tax, no nothing! Except vice and immorality galore in this International Zone of Freedom ; and a fabulous hotel, El Minzah, complete with all the trimmings of Morocco and its 'patios', so frequently met with in Spanish houses, where one could laze and lounge and drink the most potent of drinks, with guitars and dancing girls all thrown in. Very reasonable prices too—except when one came to the girls ; gold-diggers of Broadway to be sure! The Paris quarter of Montmartre had nothing on Tangier ; and the girls of course had next to nothing on either!

Business completed, I 'phoned my Alexandria friends saying there was a boat eastward-bound leaving Gib. that week, and I could be at Port Said, Egypt, in a few days, if that suited them.

Tháfne answered the 'phone saying it would be grand seeing me again, but that she and her cousin Myrtó—a pure Grecian— were off to Cairo next day, as Myrtó needed a rest ; but said that after landing at Port Said, I could easily charter a car and be through to Cairo in a matter of hours ; and we would meet at the famed Shepheard's Hotel there.

Right! so that was that ; and I was stepping off at Port Said within the week.

I had my Rainbow always in mind, with its seven spanned colours representing Love, Meekness, Sympathy, Mercy, Tolerance, Kindness and Goodness.

So I come to my next episode, Egypt ; little knowing then that another tragedy was to be unfolded.

CHAPTER 8

EGYPT AND THÁFNE

THE motor ride from Port Said, skirting Alexandria and running through the endless, hot, glaring, pitiless sandy desert, was novel, if not hair-raising ; for the Arabs seem to delight in courting death in their mad rush through space in the sand-storms caused mechanically by their terrific speed. They must have bigger big-toes than my Ceylon driver, who would have been classed as 'crawling' by their technique ! At times in that sandy wilderness one suddenly comes to a dip which is really hard to see owing to the glare, and the car, spluttering along, seemed to be travelling in mid-air ; in orbit in fact. In the desert one does not ordinarily come up against a sand-storm—a storm to our meanings—covering any large area. It seems more to hover around in pockets ; and to my mind we appeared to be in and out of pockets all the time! One can appreciate therefore, with tremendous winds that suddenly whip up, the desert is for-ever changing in its general formation ; flat here, high sand dunes there. And next day high sand dunes here, and flat there. In all, one gets an intimate feeling of one's own small individuality pitted against a tremendously vast background of desert, and nothing but desert ; and to be stranded in such barrenness one needs no vivid imagination to picture how men have died parched by the desert's sand, the glare and maddening heat.

En route we passed bands of Arabs squatting around their tents having a meal ; *the* delicacy apparently being sheeps' eyes or baby camel !

Approaching Cairo, the city looked most imposing miles away, with all its starch-white domes and minarets standing high up in relief.

45

Cairo at last, and Shepheard's Hotel, with Tháfne there at the wide entrance to greet me. It was all new and strange, for Egypt seemed so different from Ceylon. There was not the lush vegetation or foliage for one thing.

It was a great reunion, and I could sense I was more than welcome. Tháfne, not feeling sea-sick now, was 'dressed to kill'. A Greek girl with black hair, and blue, blue eyes, as I have previously detailed ; and a neat figure. She was effervescence itself ; and Myrtó (pronounced Meertó), a little older by ten years, acted as chaperon—the whiles !

We had lots to talk about ; what was Gib. like ? what was Tangier like ? and so on. I said I must see all that was to be seen in and around Cairo ; including the celebrated Arab fortune-teller, Mitzu. Later on he told me my fortune (none of which came true !) with a penetrating gaze, in a darkened room, smelling of incense ; or did that aroma come from a camel he had at the back of his tiny room ? He showed me his 'book', with pride in his heart, bearing signatures of all the crowned heads of Europe and elsewhere. Most interesting ; and in all humility, I added my own flourish!

So we began an intensive tour of old and new Cairo.

The comparatively new Cairo tower, whose base is built from rosy finished Aswan granite, is a very spectacular affair. It is about 600 feet high (150 feet taller than the Great Pyramid) and one obtains a wonderful panoramic view of all Cairo. The decorations in the entrance are most attractive and represent the new industrial and social life in the U.A.R. (United Arab Republic). It was completely designed and constructed by Egyptian technicians and materials. There is a roof-restaurant, consisting of three Halls, Harroon El-Rasheed, Al-Dawar, and the open-air garden ; the cafeteria above consists of the Arabic Hall and the Pharaonic Hall. Thence to see the Museum, where most of the Tut-an-Khamen relics lie unearthed from over 4000 years ago. Amazingly interesting ; and some of the ancient enamelling of pottery in such a richness of colour even today was breathtaking ; and made one 'furiously to think'.

Then, of course, one day to the Pyramids. We drove out there in the morning and had lunch at the fabulous Mena House Hotel near by ; and from there took camels to the Pyramids. Truly ships of the desert, these camels, and I have never been

nearer to sea-sickness on these 'ships' than on any boat afloat!
Guides helped us to dismount on to the bench-like steps—guides
in black belted gowns, beneath which dress I would not care to
look into their past lives! Nomad Arabs, I am sure they must
have been; and no sooner were we on 'terra-sanda' than we
were whisked away by these touts who commenced jabbering in
the most expert commercial style possible! Myrtó had stayed
behind, for in travelling any distance, the sun bakes down on you,
and you yearn for the shade of the palm-trees and the water that
lies so refreshingly cool beneath them; that, and the desert winds
laden with fine sand, appeared to affect her asthma. None of
us were Bedouins loving their desert homeland! Without being
unkind, I was thankful she did not come, for it gave us privacy
in the endless Egyptian desert; and at times we let the guide go
and lose himself in the innumerable subterranean passages inside
the colossal edifices.

It is a truism that

> 'Tis Love that makes our willing feet
> In swift obedience move.

I could see where I was going, but could I see where my steps
would end? For life is very queer. I had suffered much distress;
but life must go on; and whilst in the East life was cheap, I felt
that in my case life needed to be dear, and happiness was dearly
sought by me 'young in heart'—or in Gaelic *Tìr nan òg* (land of
the ever young); a sort of Peter Pan spirit and outlook, and I
must walk with the times. It was no use living in the past; it
was the future now. The Arabs still wandered in the desert as
they did countless ages ago in the Biblical days. Was I wandering
like them, I kept asking myself? Maybe; perhaps; who knew?
And as a simile, when Saul of Tarsus was suddenly arrested by that
Great Voice, he answered, 'Lord, what wilt Thou have *me* do?'

In John Bunyan's immortal dream we read of Little Faith
who, on his way to the Celestial City, was waylaid by thieves
who robbed him of the loose coins which he carried on his person.
But his jewels, which were hidden away in a secret pocket, they
could not find. With this allegory in mind, I kept a faith that one
day, be it in Egypt or elsewhere, I *would* find a jewel hidden away
at the end of the rainbow, and so in the closing years find happiness after such a long search.

But I am anticipating Time. We must return to the Present—to the Pyramids.

The PYRAMIDS are a wondrous, stupendous sight ; you are awe-struck by them, rising to such great heights alone—quite alone—in the spaceless, silent desert ; and in the moonlight they take on an eerie arresting look, and when one thinks they were built thousands and thousands of years before Christ, the whole panorama speaks of the miraculous. Supernatural you may say, and one's heart throbs in such knowledge ; and with a Grecian beauty at one's side, little wonder that Love comes under way.

Everyone who visits Egypt has heard of the Pyramids—the oldest structures of stone in all the world—but few know more about them than that they are tall and conical ; and very old. Some have an idea they were the buildings that the Children of Israel built for Pharaoh under the lash of Egyptian overseers ; but the Pyramids had been standing for more than one thousand years before the Children of Israel had ever seen Egypt.

They are tombs, the greatest tombs in the world ; tombs of kings who believed themselves gods, and nearly 5000 years ago prepared what they thought fitting to be, namely, a resting-place for themselves. Wealthy kings also, for they must have possessed vast sums to have enabled them to build such costly monuments.

One thing standing out clearly in the case of the ancient Egyptians was their belief in a continued existence after death. It was a limited immortality, for all depended on the preservation of the body from decay ; and the measures necessary were so expensive and complicated that they were not within the bounds of anyone, save the rich. The Egyptian could not conceive the spiritual part of an individual existing without a bodily tenement to contain it. The body must be treated as if it still had needs, and must be supplied with food and drink.

The preservation of the body was attended to by embalm-ment—mummification—then a strong coffin was provided which was lowered down a shaft into a chamber hewn out of rock ; the chamber walled up ; the shaft filled in, and then came the point as to how the requisite food and drink was to be provided ? A house was built above the funeral vault, and in it, or near it, was a chapel where devotees could come bringing offerings of food, flowers and water. These were then laid down before a niche in the chapel wall, shaped like a door, which should make possible for the spiritual part of the deceased—which still existed, the 'KA'—to come through the doorway and partake of such offerings.

An Egyptian tomb had therefore two distinct parts : the burial chamber below, and the chapel above. This then is the principle and the idea attached to the Pyramids. The king was to be worshipped by his people on this earth and then be received among the gods above. The kings therefore were to have a building of grandeur, the actual pyramid being the funeral vault ; the temple outside—the 'gateway temple'—being essentially for the funerary ritual ; and so against the west wall of the Pyramid was the granite false door, before which the offerings were laid.

A causeway led up to the temple from the desert.

The Great Pyramid—the Pyramid of Cheops—has withstood the changes of 5000 years so well that, despite 'explorations', it remains one of the greatest monuments of all time.

The Great Sphinx itself belongs to the second pyramid group ; it is really of an accidental nature and is not an essential to the pyramid plans as a whole. It is a spur of natural rock resembling a crouching lion. The Sphinx is a mythical animal, made up of the head of a man with the body of a lion, 'strength and wisdom'. King Chephren conceived this idea of carving the huge rock symbolical of his 'supremeness' ; and it stands watching over the entrance to his temple as a guardian god. At first the Egyptians worshipped it as a Sun God in their error.

The Sphinx is 70 feet high and 200 feet in length.

The Pyramid is 450 feet high, the length of each side measures about 700 feet ; it covers an area of 13 acres.

It is said that for the Pyramid of Cheops there were 100,000 workmen quarrying the stones in the Arabian desert and ferrying these over ; ten years were spent on building the causeway, and twenty years in building the Pyramid itself. The blocks of stone each weigh three tons and more.

The above, then, is a general description of the wonderful Pyramids, and the endless silent desert. A trip one can *never* forget ; I remember it clearly, although it is now more than twenty-five years ago. They will be there, standing as landmarks and sentinels when all of us are gone.

As Tháfne and I witnessed it all, feeling awakened by these visible reminders of the past, there were times—being so full of veneration seeing these relics of well over 5000 years ago—when we were speechless ; and when we did speak, it was in whispers. The limitlessness of Time, in the limitless desert ; the Pharaohs, the kings, and all that went to make up Destiny.   One needs go there to see for oneself—when I am certain my readers would also speak in whispers, feeling hypnotised and drugged by everything. The sunsets over the desert are beyond words ; red, brilliant red, due to the air being so charged with millions of grains of fine sand. To gaze on the Sphinx—the riddle of the Sphinx—reminds one forcibly of an age that has gone so long before us ; fifty centuries before ; and we were alive to see it—the glory of 'what was' ; and we felt like pigmies, for it fixed upon our retinas a picture of stark reality ; a picture outlasting Time.   Everything of the past many thousand years stood out before us in bold relief ; it stamped itself on our minds.   It was the attainment of the famous Arabian standard, 'He speaks the best who turns the ear into an eye'.

'If thou wouldest believe, thou shouldest see.'   In all conscience we saw ; holding hands we bent our knees, partly in awe, partly in adoration of the past.   They must have been a great people in those days ; a great nation.

There was no veil hiding these immense sentinels of the desert. Humbly, I acknowledge my imperfections in describing these structural monuments to the full ; and feel I have only touched the fringe of emotions that unquestionably come before one ; and before one's innermost thoughts.   The eye of the intellect can often see beauties, while the heart remains asleep and sees nothing at all.   But our hearts were far from being asleep.   On a silent night under a starry sky, as is so often the case in the desert, one can reflect more deeply with the noise of everyday life being stilled ; and in such solitude one comes face to face with the universe, and of a mysterious awe towards *a* Power that must surely govern this great world of ours.

We duly returned to Mena House Hotel, taking camels as before.   We did not speak ; there was no need to speak, for we had been looking deep—very deep—into Time ; before the Children of Israel's time in fact.

As we dismounted at the hotel steps, I turned and looked at the camel.   The camel always has a supercilious look—contemptuousness personified—and the most docile of them think nothing of suddenly turning and having a snap at you. More than once in the streets of Aden have I nearly had my ear taken off. As I turned and glanced at this beast, it had an inscrutable look. There are seven wonders of the world. Legend has it that Allah has entrusted to the camel what the eighth wonder of the world is ; but the camel remained as inscrutable as ever—ever since Time began. The moon was up and the tops of the Pyramids appeared dim on the far horizon in the hot night.

The view from the verandah of Mena House Hotel facing the Nile is delightful looking through the trees on the embankment to the fairy lights beyond ; the waters of the Great Nile being of a pale blue, tinted with pink—the whole having a most romantic atmosphere. The dhows sailing silently, manned by Arabs in their brightly-coloured turbans and robes, with curved daggers here and there showing at their waistbands. Simple men, holding a firm belief in Allah to whose Will, all good or all evil is attributed. Their tempo of life is full of ease ; when Allah made Time, He made plenty of it they will tell you. Very akin to the Highlands of Scotland, for patience in the Highlands is not only a virtue ; it is an integral part of daily life.

Joining cousin Myrtó, we had an apéritif ; then upstairs to wash the sand out of our system ; changed into evening dress, and down to dinner—spotless tables and appointments, shaded lights and quiet-moving Arab waiters. Then to dance, engulfing ourselves into the 20th-century way of life, leaving behind us 5000 years of bewilderment.

An American tourist near our table was showing off her souvenirs. 'I bought this scarab,' she said, 'from an Arab boy who assured me he had stolen it himself during the excavations, and I'm sure it must be genuine, because the little boy had such an honest face !'

After a wonderful ten days in Cairo, it was time to go back home (Tháfne's home) to Alexandria ; and this time we all went by train. A slow, monotonous, dusty journey ; for the Egyptian rolling-stock was primitive in those days. When we arrived at her home the native house-boy greeted her with the saying, 'the light has returned to Alex.'

In Alexandria I stayed at the Hotel Cecil, the main hotel overlooking the clear, blue Mediterranean Sea.

I thought it well to hire a car ; and Tháfne got in touch with a Greek garage who would gladly oblige.   There is an old Latin proverb ' *Timeo Danaos et dona ferentes*', meaning ' I distrust the Greeks, even when they offer gifts'; a saying I remembered from my school days and which originated from the Siege of Troy and the episode of the wooden horse which contained hidden invading soldiers.   And this proverb certainly appeared to apply to this Greek garage wallah!   The car looked fine, but seemed to lack a proper engine.   It gave a heap of trouble, so much so that Tháfne was constantly 'phoning them ; and from her voice, and judo-like antics at her end of the line, she seemed to be laying into them in fluent Greek in the manner of a sergeant-major.   I am sure there are many abusive swear words in the Greek vocabulary!   So another car was forthcoming, and it served its purpose well.

Of course, prior to all this, it was necessary to obtain a driving licence.   No British or Ceylon licence would be acceptable ; and I had to go down to the appropriate department in the native quarter of the town to fill in forms and take a test.   Although I had been driving cars for nearly twenty-five years, I had never taken a test ; so I looked upon this as another adventure.   I was ushered in (after waiting at least an hour in a queue, being bandied about next to dirty Arabs and Greeks, who too were 'on trial', and after getting a native scribe to help me fill in the Arabic forms) to a small office with an Egyptian officer gaily decked-up in khaki uniform (with medals galore) seated on a chair.   He pointed to me to sit on a rickety stool, and, with a dirty old tablespoon, covered first my left eye, then my right, asking me to read the large lettered card some twenty feet away—just as though one was having one's eyes tested at an optician's.   Am certain I didn't distinguish one-half of the letters ; I just rattled them off at random!   But I got my certificate of road-worthiness—nae bother at a'.   I think they were more concerned in getting my piastres than anything else!   Then, setting out in the car, I had to remember one drove on the RIGHT in Egypt, not the LEFT side of the road.   However, it all came quite easily and am happy to record no accidents ; and that is saying a great deal if one knows the Eastern driver.   Both in Ceylon and in Egypt there appears to be *no* rule of the road, and little courteousness on the highway.   In short, there seems to be no Highway Code east of Suez ; you make your own, and leave it at that !   I once asked a taxi-driver why he kept driving from the right-hand side of the road to the left-hand side and vice versa. His reply was there was no right or left; only sun and shade!

Well, as readers can imagine, life was sweet and easy. Tháfne's home—it was a flat with wooden shuttered windows that were closed at noon each day to keep the sun out and so help keep the rooms cooler—was nice, and cosy by Western standards. There was just herself, her Greek mother, her father, her Greek uncle, and cousin Myrtó who lived there in Rue Ste Julienne, a suburb of Alexandria, some four or five miles from the city centre. To get hot water for a bath was comical. There was a sort of geyser over the bath, but the means of heating the water was by wooden sticks, such as we light our coal fires with; and one kept feeding in bits of wood as one bathed, to keep the heat going; and the water at the best of times was only tepid. It was quite a thought to keep getting in and out of the bath to feed in a few more sticks —to keep the home fires burning! The bedrooms had high archaic beds, and one needed a foot-stool to help you get into them! But who cared!

We used to frequent the Alex. Sporting Club, a very fashionable meeting-place, where one saw all the élite of the town, the women all dressed up in latest Paris gowns; wonderful food, wonderful music, wonderful prices, and—wonderful women, mostly Greeks. Sometimes after lunching there we would play a round of golf on the Club's private course. All the 'greens' were of sand, watered and rolled daily. Amazing what one's golf ball will do in putting on a 'sand' green, when one has been accustomed to grass 'greens'. At first it took me about a dozen putts or so, even though I had landed only a yard from the hole. Most amusing; and as I was wearing spiked shoes, I had to take them off when coming to the 'greens', and putt out in my stocking feet! But then our games were not serious. It was just something to do until evening, when we invariably went to one of the select dancing clubs, where again, a plethora of beautiful Greek women were to be seen in their startling gowns and jewellery; beauty of a kind rarely seen in England; and my partner was a Grecian girl already likened to Helen of Troy. When in her black evening dress, with a low neckline showing a discreet 'cleavage', and be-jewelled, perhaps I should couple to that likeness, the Queen of Sheba.

Solomon and the Queen of Sheba!—Queen of Arabia as we would know it in our day. What a spectacular meeting *that* must have been!

There is a legend relating to Solomon and the queen that—so far as I know—has not appeared in print. It was given me by an Arab amidst the desert's vastness. We have it on record that Solomon had wisdom and understanding exceeding that of all the east country. Not only wise, he was subtle and loved many strange women, together with the daughter of Pharaoh ; women of the Moabites, Ammonites, Edomites, Zidonians and Hittites. And when the Queen of Sheba, hearing of his fame, paid her famous visit to him, bringing with her a very great train of servants, camels, spices, gold, precious stones and the like, Solomon fell in love with her ; but his advances were persistently rebuked. After a while he instructed his cooks to set before the queen a highly spiced and thirst-producing dish. He also ordered that all the fountains in his palace, both inside and out, be turned off—save the one in his large and ornate bedroom.

The legend goes on to say the queen awoke at midnight with a burning thirst and frantically wandered all over the palace in search of water. She found none, but eventually heard the sound of a fountain playing in the king's bedroom—and rushed in to quench her thirst. Within the space of a year, when the queen had returned to her own country, a son was born ; and accordingly all Ethiopians proudly claim to be descendants of Solomon.

With a car, we were able to take many outings and jaunts into the countryside ; and my recollections of looking at the Mediterranean in the evenings with no one around save Tháfne, were entrancing to say the least. The blue sea and a moon take a lot of beating! In the countryside, whenever we stopped, there always seemed to be some Arab peasant appearing from behind a hedge ; and coming across to the car, would put his hand inside his robes saying, 'Master want any saucy postcards of dancing girls ?' What a question, when he could see I was otherwise engaged on pressing business! Tháfne would tell me to send him away, but seemingly he knew no English—or did he ? She said, speak just one word of Arabic to him, '*Imshi*' (meaning 'go away'), and you'll find he'll vanish. (Yes, Tháfne knew Greek and Arabic

fluently—a good friend to have around.) On one occasion I said
to an Arab, 'Imshi', making myself out to have a fluent Arabic
tongue! To our surprise, he said in English, 'Imshi? Why should
I "imshi"; this is my country!' Collapse of Bee Jay; collapse
of Tháfne; and hastily I pressed the self-starter, put in the clutch
and away we went. What a laugh it gave us! I wonder why
there should be so many inquisitive beggars in these foreign lands?
I am happy to say, up in Wester Ross, one is not worried or em-
barrassed by such intruders as these; one has all the glens and the
bracken to oneself!

Yes, the time easily passed on these outings; bathes on sandy
beaches (Tháfne, a lithe golden figure in a pale yellow one-piece
bathing-suit), picnic lunches and so forth; just we two, for there
was no line of demarcation as in Ceylon.

The days slipped by all too quickly, as such days do; and after
four or five weeks' sojourn in Alex. I said I must be thinking of
going back to England again, to sort out my affairs and prepare
for retirement in earnest. Although in love, Tháfne did not wish
to be engaged just then; she felt she wanted a few more months
to arrange her life; but pledged her great love for me; that she
would come to England with Pater—for Mater would not take
the journey at her age—and we would be married. We left each
other in no doubts—no doubts whatsoever—and although she
was partially Greek, I believed her, for I had had many oppor-
tunities of testing our love whilst in Egypt.

I felt this was the middle of the rainbow, and wondered if it
could well mean the end of the rainbow? There was no reason
at all why it should not be so.

I left Alex. on the morning train to catch the boat at Port
Said. I 'phoned Rue Ste Julienne from there, to learn all was well,
and that certainly within the next six months she would sail . . .

> Red sails in the sunset, 'way over the sea,
> Oh! bring back my loved one, home safely to me . . .

was the hit tune of that time. The words held a real meaning to
us both.

I sailed from Egypt that midnight, and had an uneventful
journey home.

Of course all I have written of Egypt, except the Tower of
Cairo, was long before President Gamal Abdel Nasser came to

power. I was talking recently to an Egyptian student over on a three-year study of geology at Glasgow University, who told me Nasser was doing a great job in Egypt; and spoke of him in glowing terms. So to President Nasser and his colleagues at the spectacular Presidential Palace building in Cairo—*Slàinte Mhath!* Egypt is a wonderful country to visit, and tourists are given a warm welcome. Both Cairo and Alexandria are superb cities; they, the Nile and the Pyramids, cannot fail to leave an indelible picture in one's mind for years to come. Yes, Egypt and the land of the Pharaohs should undoubtedly be seen.

Then there came much uneasiness over Italy (Mussolini) and Abyssinia and the Ethiopian Emperor at Addis-Ababa, with the result we all know of Mussolini's 'triumphant' invasion of Abyssinia; of imminent 'sanctions' by the British Government against Italy, which never came to anything, and which Mussolini scorned. It was altogether an appalling episode in recent history. Tháfne at that time was making all her preparations, and she and Pater were so looking forward to coming to England, and to the 'coming event' (the wedding; not a baby, I'd have you know!) One of her letters at the time spoke of much alertness in Alex. and Cairo of the Royal Air Force. All the British lads were standing by, and 'planes kept fully serviced; everything at action stations. But of course this was only the British lion yawning; it was not even stretching itself, let alone showing its claws; and Mussolini just laughed. The far-flung British Empire, the Empire 'on which the sun never sets'—as we were taught in history classes of my youth—was a myth. The days of Clive of India in the 18th century, and of Britain's tough spirit, were over and done with; exploded. Mussolini got away with it all; and Emperor Haile Selassie became an exile for several years.

It was all very disturbing; and of course Tháfne and Pater were anxious and afraid to leave Mater and Myrtó behind. I could appreciate their troubled minds; mine too was more than troubled, and I thought of flying out to them. She was so dear in my heart, for Paradise was beckoning, and I looked upon Tháfne as the eighth wonder of the world (the other seven being the Pyramids; the Hanging Gardens of Babylon; the Tomb of Mausolus at Halicarnassus in Asia Minor; the Temple of Diana at Ephesus; the Colossus of Rhodes; the Statue of Jupiter

Olympus ; and the Pharos of Alexandria—a marble watch-tower and lighthouse on the island of Pharos in the harbour of Alex.).

Whilst I was planning this, it so happened one day, one of Mussolini's bombers was forced back from its Abyssinian raid. In flying over the Red Sea, and passing Suez, it cut across via Cairo and Alexandria—the shortest way back to its base in Italy. In passing over Alexandria, somehow or other—it was never explained why—a spare bomb accidentally was let loose.

It fell on Rue Ste Julienne. . . .

Once again my rainbow in the sky was blotted out by tears. In Greek I uttered,

oti eíné na Gínni, tha Gínni ;

and in Arabic,

zei ma tígi, tígi.

Truly, 'Whatever will be, will be'.

E

CHAPTER 9

NORTH-WEST TO MULL

I WAS in Scotland again.

Oft-times I would think, that never blooms the rose so red, as where some buried Caesar bled. And once again, old Khayyám's Rubáiyát would tell me the 'Moon of my Delight who know'st no wane, the Moon of Heav'n is rising once again'; that, and to make the most of what we yet may spend, before we too into the Dust descend—*sans* laughter, *sans* song, *sans* love, *sans* end; yes, and *sans* everything.

When I heard of Tháfne's death my head fell to one side, and I seemed to pass away also. The silver cord was loosed; the golden bowl broken. The sorrow of death compassed me. It was a sore dispensation. I felt I was the branch which fell with the untimely end of the tree; or as an aged tree that had been struck with lightning, standing stript of its leaves—just a monument on the earth. The grass withered, the flower faded; I had become like a hart that finds no pasture.

The enamel on the little trinket box belonging to Pharaoh's age, that I had obtained in Cairo, had suddenly lost its sheen.

I was up in Gairloch, Ross-shire, still in search of my eternal site; away from the land of waving palms, and of natives constantly waving their 'palms' too ('alms for the love of Allah'), and living in the land of *Slàinte Mhath*. At this stage the Second World War had broken loose on us all; and being still on the youngish side, I was glad to be able to serve in the war effort, in working in conjunction with the Ministry of Fuel and Power, controlling a score of works all over Scotland. Ceylon and Egypt were 'way back in my mind, for there was much to do; so much at stake if we were to emerge as victors over an evil régime—a régime where there would be no place for Hope. But for Winston Churchill, I feared we would have gone under; his words were always an inspiration, for he had hope and courage as no man. For is it not written, we are saved by hope; for on

earth there is no place for despair. Being more matured, I felt
if I were spared, and peace *did* come along, I would embrace
life anew ; and my faith enabled me to believe that later on I
would find rest and contentment—and above all, love—at the end
of the rainbow. For Love is 'a many splendoured thing'. The
past—and who of us have no pasts ?—needs be forgotten ; it *has*
to be so. There is an old Sanskrit saying :

> The Past is a Dream,
> The Future a vision ;
> 'Tis the Present, well spent, that matters. . . .

Whilst in Tháfne's death there were tears, the love involved
evoked inspiration. Very often out of sorrow there comes gladness. If one be sad, one's prayers do not rise up to the altar of
God—for sadness is still in the heart ; and so one therefore needs
to put sadness from one's soul. To everything there is a season,
and a time to every purpose ; a time to weep, and a time to
laugh ; a time to mourn, and a time to dance. I looked upwards and onwards, sensing all would come right in the years
ahead ; especially as I had a Paradise in view in Wester Ross—
in Gairloch—which became a reality in 1960.

After the peace of 1945, I was constantly up in the west
coast at Gairloch for several months each summer. Gairloch
was the goal ; and in due course, it came to pass.

In my journeys up north I invariably turned off at Tyndrum
(the house on the ridge)—pronounced Tyne-drum—via Glencoe,
for the Caledonian Canal, and Inverness ; and then onwards and
westwards to the sea ; passing dearly-loved Garve, Achnasheen,
Loch Maree, thence to Gairloch. Having given a full description
of this 'royal route' north from Edinburgh in my other book,
there is no need to enlarge upon all that great journey here again ;
and of the many points of special interest one comes across in that
route.

On this particular trip in 1957, as my project at Gairloch was
not quite under way, I decided to veer left at Tyndrum and make
for Oban, instead of Glencoe, for during the war I was often in
that town and thought it a very likeable place. Years previously,
the bay would be full of a galaxy of yachts from millionaires
downwards. It used to be the 'Cowes' of Scotland ; moreover,
I had friends in Mull, at the 'White House of Aros', situate

just south of Tobermory, and many times they had asked me
to pay them a visit during the summer months they were in
residence.

Accordingly, I followed the sign-post TYNDRUM TO OBAN,
37 miles ; a good road, fairly straight, passing Dalmally (13 miles),
Loch Awe, through the Pass of Brander to Taynuilt, and Connel
Ferry—5 miles out of Oban.

I was bound for Mull . . . paying my respects to Oban *en
passant*.

Just a mile or so beyond the large Loch Awe Hotel, on the left,
is Saint Conan's Kirk ; a wonderful piece of workmanship that
no one should miss seeing. You suddenly come upon it on
the loch side of the main Oban road.

SAINT CONAN'S, nestling amongst the tall trees, the loch, and
complete stillness is a thing of beauty ; a masterpiece of craftsmanship—in fact it is one of the show-pieces of Argyll, and is both
old and new.

St. Conan was the patron saint of Lorne, and reputed to have
lived in Glenorchy, which is the glen running between the Dalmally road we have taken and the Glencoe road. He was a
disciple, though not a contemporary, of St. Columba, and, like
him, came from Ireland. As a young man he was chosen to be
tutor to the two sons of the King of Scotland, and eventually rose
to be a bishop. A legend around his name has given rise to an
old Highland proverb, as follows : like many of the Celtic saints,
St. Conan was not afraid to meet the devil face to face. On one
such occasion they met to discuss the fate of the souls of the people
of Lorne, and they went about it in a thoroughly businesslike
fashion, for they divided everyone—not into sheep and goats—but
into three categories : the really good, the downright bad, and
those in-between or 'the middling'. The good were to be the
saints, and the bad the devils. The middling were to be shared
equally ; and this sharing was to be done by drawing in turn.
All went placidly until the devil got excited and stretched out his
hand when it was the saint's turn. St. Conan would not allow
that and he rapped his adversary smartly over the knuckles, saying,
'Na, na ; fair play ; paw for paw' ; and this phrase has come
down the ages in the Highlands as a proverb.

Up till the 1870's, although the road from Stirling to Oban
passed along the north shore of Loch Awe, there were practically

no human habitations between Dalmally and Taynuilt. But with the arrival of the railway, the loch became less inaccessible.

The hotel was then built, and one, Walter Douglas Campbell, younger brother of the 1st Lord Blythswood, bought the island of Innischonain on Loch Awe from the Marquis of Breadalbane, on which he built a large mansion, settling there with his mother and his sister Helen. But his mother found the journey to Dalmally to the church there too troublesome; and so her son decided to build her a church near by.

Walter Campbell was a man of many talents, all of which he devoted to this kirk. He was a most capable architect, a collector of works of art and a skilled woodcarver.

The original church was begun in 1881 and finished in 1886, and was a comparatively small, simple building. It occupied what is now the nave, and a part of the choir of the present kirk. But he was not satisfied; he began to dream of a far nobler building and started work on same in 1907, devoting the rest of his life to its execution. He died in 1914, and work had to be suspended during the First World War; but as soon as practicable, his sister Helen carried out the plans he had left. When she died in 1927, the Trustees finally completed the project.

No labour was brought in from outside, and the stone of which the church was built was not quarried, but consisted of boulders lying on the slopes of the hill above, which were rolled down, split, and shaped on the spot—a Herculean task.

Campbell was his own architect, and he was not hemmed in by ordinary conventions, for he was more anxious to achieve beauty than consistency.

The view from the sun-dial terrace on the south side is one of the most beautiful in Argyll, and it was this which determined the site of the church. Immediately below are the waters of Loch Awe; away to the north-east rises Ben Lui, snow-capped for half the year, overlooking the three glens of the Lochy, the Orchy and the Strae.

The church has no level foundation, but clings to the steep hillside, with the result the southern face is built upon terraces and retaining walls dropping far below the floor levels. It was on this lofty façade he spent long hours evolving in his mind the building that was to 'come to pass'. It would be the memory of the long days so spent that inspired the inscription on the dial, 'Until the

day break, and the shadows flee away' (Song of Solomon iv. 6) ;
and on the surrounding parapet, 'Thy sun shall no more go down'
(Isaiah lx. 20).

Inside the church may be seen many heavy oak beams taken
from two famous old battleships, the *Caledonia* and the *Duke of
Wellington*. Wood from these ships was also used for the doors,
and some of the roofwork of the main building.

In one of the many chapels is a vault which contains the
remains of the builders, Walter Campbell and his sister. The
figure on the tomb is that of Campbell himself, and the text
carved round the wall reads, 'And the Lord spake, saying, let
them make me a sanctuary ; that I may dwell among them'
(Exodus xxv. 8). Surely most apposite.

Some of the chapels are protected by most beautiful wrought-
iron gates, bearing the initials and badges of those who lie beneath
—exquisite craftsmanship.

At the far end of the aisle there are two stained-glass windows.
The first, which contains the Royal Arms blazoned with those of
Argyll, is in memory of H.R.H. The Princess Louise, daughter
of Queen Victoria, and wife of the late Duke of Argyll. The
Blythswood family were on intimate terms with the Princess, who
took a great personal interest in the building of St. Conan's.
Doubtless it is due to her that the marble bust of the young Queen
Victoria—which faces the pulpit—was brought here.

The Bruce chapel owes its origin to the fact that it was on
the hillside above the church that the king despatched his famous
outflanking column under the Earl of Douglas, which inflicted
such a decisive defeat upon John of Lorne and his clansmen in the
Pass of Brander (towards Taynuilt). The effigy—which is more
than life-size—is of wood, the face and hands being of alabaster,
and was the work of an Edinburgh sculptor who was also respon-
sible for the figure of St. Conan outside the church near the sun-
dial looking across the loch to the mountains beyond. This same
sculptor designed the War Memorial at the entrance gate to the
kirk. Beneath the figure, let into the base, is a small ossuary
which contains a bone of the king himself, taken from Dunferm-
line Abbey.

But it is perhaps the Apse, and ambulatory with the immense
solid pillars, narrow arches and clear-glass windows, that is to my
mind the most distinctive feature of St. Conan's. It is breath-

taking. The wonderful windows receive the full blaze of daylight, and have as the background the mountains of Glenorchy and Glenstrae. It presents a unique result. Within the curve of the Apse is the communion table, made of solid oak. Once again, the craftsmen were found locally, and are still represented in the village. The wood from which this table was carved weighed over seven hundredweights.

Another striking feature of the kirk is the double row of darkcarved stalls in the chancel. They were carved from Spanish chestnut, and show the full coats-of-arms, complete with crests and badges of the chiefs, who in the old days held land in the neighbourhood.

There is a fine oriel window in the chancel which lightens the library and the font. This latter is a beautiful model of a fishingboat, and is one of those which Breton fishermen hang up in their churches as votive offerings in gratitude for escaping from storms at sea.

Another interesting feature is the large organ screen : again a piece of Walter Campbell's work. The lower panels represent creatures of pagan times, whilst above same is a belt of ribbonwork symbolising Eternity. Higher still are crosses in Celtic work representing Christian times, and at the top of the screen are emblems of the four Heavenly creatures : the Lion, the Calf, the Man and the Eagle (Rev. iv. 7).

And for a climax to a most remarkable, fascinating and deeply reverential building is high above the large organ screen a beautiful painted-glass window with figures of angels and cherubs which Miss Helen Campbell designed and painted with her own hands.

This church *must* be seen to be believed ; and I feel sure no one who visits it can deny that the founder's vision of building 'To the glory of God, a House Beautiful' has indeed been realised.

The Nave is regularly used for public worship every Sunday.

Proceeding onwards, we come, as I have said, to Connel Ferry—an imposing steel cantilever railway bridge (a miniature of the Forth Bridge, and the largest of its type in Europe after the Forth Bridge), with an 8-foot pathway running alongside the single railway track line, and which takes one across the small entrance stretch of the sea loch, Loch Etive, to the coast-line road to South Ballachulish (38 miles), passing through the Benderloch district and Appin. This latter village was the scene of the notorious 'Appin murder' many years ago ; and of Robert Louis Stevenson's *Kidnapped*. In Appin they say 'sorrow's stain still lies', for there are men who know the name of the man who killed 'The Red Fox' ; and it is *not* the name of James Stewart of the Glens, who hanged at Ballachulish for that dark ambush in the wood of Lettermore.

This Benderloch district—only 9 miles from Oban—is almost surrounded by water. To the north is Loch Creran ; to the south Loch Etive ; to the west Loch Nell, or generally called Ardmucknish Bay ; and the run from Connel to South Ballachulish is a most pleasant one ; for you get unequalled views over the hills of Kerrera across to the heights of Mull. And in the summer, sunsets of a rare order.

For Oban, of course, you do not pass over this bridge, but continue straight on, leaving the 'ferry' on your right. Although you drive your car over that 300-yard bridge, barely taking a minute, a charge of between 4s. and 6s. (plus 2d. per person) is levied over this toll bridge. The ferry, or bridge, is always open. Near by the bridge, the Falls of Lora present a pretty picture when in full flood. These 'Falls' are more in the nature of rapids, caused by a barrier running across the mouth of Loch Etive. At low tide this barrier is a mere six feet below the surface of the loch, with higher points projecting. At high tide the whole ridge is submerged, but as the tide ebbs, the whole volume of Loch Etive rolls and tumbles through its narrow outlet, to form the water race which has for centuries been known as the 'Falls of Lora'.

Five miles from Connel is Oban ; and there we tarry a while.

CHAPTER 10

OBAN

OBAN, and the Land of Lorne ; and a stepping-off place to Mull ; and although I did not know it at the time, I was heading for Romance—for the 'end of the rainbow'.

The town has a resident population of about 7000 ; when such events as THE MOD take place, that figure can easily be increased to 17,000.

Oban is the 'Charing Cross of the Highlands'.

It is a modern town, for but a century or so ago it was only a fishing hamlet, with a little primitive farming. One can find plenty to do there : steamers going to many places of interest, Mull, Staffa, Iona, Fort William (the start of the Caledonian Canal) ; and motor drives down pretty, restful country to Lochgilphead, Crinan Canal, Ardrishaig, and then up by Inveraray (and the Duke of Argyll's castle) and back via Loch Awe, Taynuilt and Connel again—a circular tour of about 100 miles, that one should certainly take.

In the early days of the century, Oban was a most fashionable resort, with the bay crowded with luxury yachts, as I have said. Today there are less of such yachts, less aristocracy ; more of the plebeian characteristics ; albeit Oban is the headquarters of the Royal Highland Yacht Club.

The name, Oban, has given rise many times to speculation. Most Gaelic speakers seem to think Oban means the 'little bay' ; the first part being Norse, and the '—an', a Gaelic ending meaning 'little'. On the other hand, there are some who think it is derived from a liaison of the two Gaelic words, '*ob*' and '*ban*'—resulting in 'the white bay'. However, Oban could hardly mean this, for if it did, the end of the word would be pronounced as '*baan*'. Besides, the bay is far from white !

Oban is a town set in a land of ancient history, ruined castles still speaking of the days when the Lords of Lorne defied kings with impunity. The hills of Lorne slope gently to the wonderful crescent-shaped bay, sheltered from the Atlantic's west winds by the long, green fertile island of Kerrera, beyond which are the heights of Morvern (sometimes spelt Morven), the name given to that part of the mainland of Scotland south of Ardnamurchan, fringing the sky-line separated by the blue waters of the Sound of Mull from the Isle of Mull, whose towering hills seem to rise from the ocean's bed.

On Kerrera, Alexander II of Scotland died in 1249. Whilst engaged in a punitive expedition against some of the disloyal Lords of the West, he fell ill of a fever and was carried ashore to die at a point still known as Dalrigh (the King's Field), just beyond the Kerrera end of the ferry. Beneath where he died is a picturesque bay known as the Horse-shoe Bay ; and here some years later King Haakon of Norway sheltered his fleet prior to his setting forth to Largs, where in the subsequent engagement his fleet was destroyed and the domination of Norway over the west of Scotland finally broken. At the southern end of this island stands the ruins of Gylen Castle, which in its day guarded that end of the sound of Kerrera, as did Dunollie Castle the northern end. Both these castles belonged to the MacDougalls of Lorne. By reason of this clan's allegiance to the Crown, it was stormed in 1647 and burnt to the ground by Parliamentary troops.

The monument clearly seen at the tip of Kerrera was erected to the memory of David Hutcheson, who with his partners did much in the development of steam communications among the Western Highlands and Islands. Messrs. G. & J. Burns were one of the Companies operating the West Highland trade (before MacBrayne's came along), but having so many other interests, they handed over this trade in 1851 to Mr. Hutcheson, who was their chief clerk, on condition that their nephew, David MacBrayne, became one of the partners. The firm of David Hutcheson & Company was founded, the partners being David Hutcheson, his brother Alex. Hutcheson and David MacBrayne.

This, then, was the beginning of the Company as we know it today—David MacBrayne Ltd. The 'Wells-Fargo' of the Western Isles! (A full and interesting account of this firm's rise to the greatness it is today is given in *And It Came to Pass*.)

I have mentioned Dunollie Castle, situate as a sentinel to the northern entrance of the bay. It was the ancient stronghold of the Lords of Lorne, Barons, once so powerful they could lay claim to one-third of the whole of Scotland. It is still the property of a descendant of that family, Mrs. MacDougall of MacDougall being the present chief, whose family tree has as deep roots as any other in the country ; and they reside in the mansion under shadow of the castle. The MacDougalls were hereditary enemies of Robert Bruce, afterwards King of Scotland. They were connected by marriage with the famous Comyns. When the fortunes of the latter were low and the Scottish circlet of gold had not yet been placed on his head, Bruce, after suffering defeat by the English at Methven, retreated to the fastness of the Western Highlands. Whilst the English were unable to pursue him, the Comyn's kinsman, MacDougall, resolved to do battle with him in a terrain every inch of which he knew. MacDougall and Bruce met each other at a spot near Tyndrum, and in a short, sharp encounter, Bruce only saved his life by parting with his plaid, into which was fastened the famous Brooch of Lorne—one of the finest pieces of ancient Scotch silver now existing. This triumph was short lived, for on gaining ascendancy in Scotland, Bruce marched against the MacDougalls and practically annihilated the clan near the Bridge of Awe in the Pass of Brander. This overwhelming defeat of that clan was followed by a ravaging of the territory of the MacDougalls.

When Bruce was crowned king he remembered the MacDougalls ; yet the brooch was treasured until its disappearance in 1647 when Castle Gylen, as I have said, was burned. All hope of recovering the brooch was abandoned, but in 1823—over 175 years later—it mysteriously reappeared in an auction sale in London, when it was presented by the Campbells to MacDougall of MacDougall, its rightful owner. Where the brooch had been all those years no one seems to know. It rests today in the mansion house of Dunollie.

Some four miles out of Oban on the Connel road there is a still more interesting castle—that of Dunstaffnage. Originally belonging to the MacDougalls, on their conquest by King Robert the Bruce it was given the status of a Royal Castle, and placed under the guardianship of the all-powerful Campbells. To it, the Scots in their wanderings from Ireland, it is said, brought the famous STONE OF DESTINY (fully dealt with, and its daring removal from Westminster Abbey on Christmas Day 1950 by a close friend of mine living near me, in *And It Came to Pass*). In the

9th century this palladium of the Scots was moved to Scone, near Perth ; and upon it the Kings of Scotland were crowned for over five hundred years. When Edward I of England (known as 'Hammer of the Scots'—and one of the early Norman kings of England) laid a despoiling hand upon the Scottish kingdom, he took the Stone, along with the ancient records of Scotland, to his capital at London in 1296 ; where it still remains. The year 1603 saw the fulfilment of the ancient prophecy, when James VI, son of Mary Queen of Scots, as King of England, succeeded to the united thrones of the two kingdoms as James I. Our present monarchy is in the line of that ancient prophetic succession.

With the removal of the Scottish Court from Dunstaffnage to Scone, the glory of the ancient palace sadly diminished, but it features once again in history in August 1746, when for a few days the immortal Flora Macdonald—without whose aid Bonnie Prince Charlie would have fallen into the hands of his enemies— was held a prisoner. I refer to 'Flora' later ; she was freed in July the following year.

Surmounting Oban's highest hill, the McCaig Tower, a granite edifice, is probably the most striking architectural feature of the entire neighbourhood. It has a remarkable resemblance to the Colosseum at Rome, though it differs from this in that whilst the Colosseum is oval, McCaig's tower is an exact circle ; and whereas the Roman structure has semicircular headed windows, this has pointed ones. It was erected in the 1890's by John Stuart McCaig, a prosperous local banker, and is probably the earliest example of a work for the relief of unemployment. Wonderful views of Lorn, Mull and Morvern, and the glistening waters surrounding them, can be seen from its unglazed windows. This edifice is sometimes referred to as 'McCaig's Folly'!

For visitors' enjoyment, mention should be made of the magnificent stretch of clear, smooth golden sands at Ganavan, some two miles from the town's centre. This beach has one of the finest natural bathing places on the west of Scotland, set in beautiful surroundings. In the foreground are the calm waters of Loch Linnhe, with the low elongated green island of Lismore in the near distance, with its lighthouse forming a sentinel to the Sound of Mull. Further off in the background are the heights of Mull and the bluff mountains of Morvern.

A large pavilion tea-room is at hand ; bathing-boxes and

small boats can be hired ; and adjoining the sands is a 6-hole golf-course (Municipal) and a caravan holiday parking ground.

Other attractions to Oban are boating, water ski-ing, golf—an 18-hole course at Glencruitten, near Mossfield Park, half a mile from town centre—fishing, tennis (eight *en-tout-cas* courts) and bowling. Oban possesses a fine Pipe Band which, during the summer months, plays thrice weekly in the Corran Parks, situate off the Esplanade on the way to Ganavan.

Previously I have mentioned the Crinan Canal, which is only an hour's run south of Oban ; and as I had a little time to spare before embarking for Mull, I went down there to spend an hour or so, turning off the main road at Cairnbaan, for the seven miles to Crinan itself. The run along the Canal banks was an exceptionally pleasant one ; and later on Fiona—whom you are to meet soon—and I, also did the same journey after the few days we spent at the Mod (Chapter 15). The Canal was cut around 1790–1800 to enable small cargo boats—'puffers'—to travel from Loch Gilp (at Lochgilphead)—which is a small inlet off Loch Fyne (of kipper renown !)—to the western seaboard (the Sound of Jura) without having to encounter the usually very stormy and long sail (about 150 miles) round the Mull of Kintyre. It is still very much in use by the Loch Fyne herring fleet bound for the fishing grounds in the Minch. We also saw many yachts taking this ideal passage to Oban. At the end of the canal, Crinan village, there is a very fine hotel at the water's edge, noted for good food and all modern conveniences.

Inveraray, too, is a very interesting old port. It is the capital of the Campbell country, and was the birthplace of author Neil Munro. Inveraray originally nestled around the 15th-century castle, later to be rebuilt in the 18th century ; and today the town still retains its ancient charm. It was at Inveraray that most of the scenes televised a few years ago in the 'Para Handy' series were 'shot'.

Nine centuries ago, the Campbells came to Argyll, and the judicious 'matches' they made formed the basis of power of the Hapsburgs of the Highlands, as I have heard them called. Many famous beauties married into the house of Argyll, the most notable being Elizabeth Gunning (an Irish rose), wife of the fifth duke. It is said when she was duchess, Inveraray Castle was a palace worthy of the Kings of Scotland ; and there was a total defiance of expense.

Of interest to visitors generally, it may serve of use to record some of the prominent events as under :

Local Mod	Held first Friday in June.
Lorn Agricultural Show	First Saturday in August.
Oban Regatta Week	First week of August.
Oban/Lorn Horticultural Show	Last week of August.
Oban Highland Games	Second week of September.
Oban Cattle Market	First two weeks of October.

Other Highland Games which can be readily visited from Oban are held in Tobermory (Mull), third Thursday of July ; and at Taynuilt, second Saturday of August. Displays of Highland recreational activities are given regularly in Oban during summer months, and include Piping, Dancing, Tossing the Caber, Shinty, etc.

The first Gaelic Mod was held in the year 1892, and at Oban. (I refer to The Mod in a later chapter.) The AN COMUNN GAIDHEALACH—the Gaelic Association—was founded in Oban the previous year, 1891, by four local Gaelic citizens : John Campbell, John MacMaster Campbell, Hugh MacCowan and Dougal MacIsaac. And a suitable plaque was unveiled at Oban at the Mod held there in October 1962.

This then, in essence, is Oban ; but I must now take leave of this lovely seaside resort and cross over to Mull, where Fiona comes into the picture by way of a chance meeting—and the course of history was changed in so far as my own crowded life was concerned. Later on, Fiona and I spent a few joyous days in Oban during Mod week.

ISLE OF MULL

CHAPTER II

MULL AND FIONA

OBAN TO MULL; and here I was to fall in love at the end of my rainbow; and my fair queen 'in ophir gold, and with embroideries of gold, her garments wrought' was to be at my right hand.

It was as much a prayer as a prophecy indeed.

Mull, in the County of Argyll, is one of the most fascinating of the major islands of the Inner Hebrides. Mull and Iona; the latter famous small island is separated from the south-west coast of Mull by a narrow sound, about half a mile across. At one time it would be linked to Mull.

Iona's charm lies in the life and work of one single man . . .

The year was 1957; the month—May; and after staying a few days in Oban, I embarked for the Isle of Mull. I took Mac-Brayne's steamer *Claymore*, a 1024-ton vessel, beautifully equipped and most seaworthy; spacious cabins lined with polished wood-work, and a chic stewardess coming in with morning tea—so different from the old *Claymore* of 726 tonnage (built 1881 and broken up in 1931) on which I had first sailed and saw Gairloch,

Wester Ross, in 1914, as mentioned in my previous book. The new *Claymore* ranks next to the *Loch Seaforth*, 1090 tons, which operates the Stornoway run from Kyle and Mallaig.

I left Oban (sleeping on board overnight) at 6.30 in the morning, arriving promptly on time—9.0 a.m.—at Tobermory (28 miles by sea from Oban), and stepped off the gangway after having a good breakfast on board. It was a Friday; on other days the vessel puts in at Craignure, Salen, Loch Aline (meaning 'beautiful loch') on the Morvern mainland, and then Tobermory. I took a taxi for the two miles to 'The White House of Aros', just off the main Tobermory-Salen road, and through the hamlet of Aros. This name-place should not be confused with Aros Castle, eight miles further down the main road near Salen.

My friends hailed me with a delight approaching that of the prodigal son returning from outer space, for they had had nobody seeing them—not even the 'locals'—since they had come over in March. In fact they had become almost speechless.

It was a biggish house; plain with regular features, and as per its name, nicely whitewashed all over. It had a fine open vista, looking right across Calve Island (which guards and protects Tobermory harbour) and the Sound of Mull to the Morvern country on the mainland; one could see the village of Lochaline across the sea; a village where there are quarries for silica sand used in glass-making. And on clear nights one could see the twinkling lights of Oban.

Whilst alluding to 'Aros' I might conveniently draw readers' attention to Aros Castle, near Salen, which was once the seat of the MacDougalls; Lords of the Isles—the uncrowned rulers of the West, who governed like despots and fought their own wars. Aros was at one time the greatest castle in Mull; older than Duart Castle further down the coast by some 14 miles, just past Craignure. Aros was probably built about A.D. 1100.

The last time the castle was officially used was in 1608, when Lord Ochiltree, Lieutenant of the Isles under James VI, anchored his flagship, the *Moon*, in Salen bay. The island chiefs were invited to the castle, and then all but two, who were known to be royalists, were asked to dine on board. At the end of the dinner, Lord Ochiltree rose, ostensibly to propose the king's health; instead he told them they were prisoners. The chiefs were imprisoned in Scottish strongholds for one year, after which they were set free under terms of the 'Statutes of Iona', which formed the beginning of the loyalty of the island chiefs to the House of Stuart.

Before I dwell on the details connected with the great and abiding love that came my way in Mull, it may be well to give a brief general survey of the island ; for visitors who journey across from Oban for a few days will wish to know more about what there is to be seen, and what the island offers, than straightway be plunged into someone else's love affair!

Mull is the third largest of the Western Islands ; and Tobermory is its capital with a population of 700. It is situate, as recorded before, about two hours' sail from Oban ; and as a rule the journey is a sheltered one, for the sea passage is almost landlocked.

Mull signifies 'a mass of hill', and is of volcanic origin. The climate is genial and bracing ; the scenery typical Hebridean, and it has a winding coast line of some 300 miles. Much tradition is attached to it from olden times when the clansmen battled for supremacy and the Lords of the Isles just named were undisputed chieftains. Its highest mountain is Ben More, 3169 feet in height, a 'Munro' (Sir Hugh Thomas Munro, b. 1856, died March 1919, compiled a table of all the mountains in Scotland of 3000 feet height and over, which has since been universally accepted as a standard for Scottish mountains), known in the Gaelic as *Beinn Mhore Muile*. This mountain is of a more gentle character than the renowned Cuillins of Skye. From its summit one has a wide vision : the north of Ireland, the Outer Hebrides including Barra, Skye, Ben Nevis (Britain's highest mountain), and of course the islands of Rum, Eigg and Muck (reminding one of a new cocktail name!) to the north ; Coll and Tiree, Staffa and Iona. And across to the south, the islands of Colonsay and Oronsay ; and the Paps of Jura. A broad vista to be sure.

Looking at the map of Mull—shown herein—it can be seen to be almost cut into two parts. At Salen on the east side, bordering the Sound of Mull, it is only separated by two miles on its western seaboard—to Loch-nan-Ceall ; so that on this line of demarcation one can describe the island figuratively as North and South Mull. The former has gentler and milder scenic beauty than the southern part, which has a mountainous terrain (with Ben More) and

F

many sea lochs, cliffs and reefs on the coast line. The south-western area, a narrow peninsula bordering on Iona, is termed the Ross of Mull. From this quarter came the red granite rock used in the building of Westminster Bridge and the Albert Memorial.

This, then, is the general lay-out of Mull, which has a total population of just over 2000.

Tobermory, the capital town of the island, is the only Burgh on Mull, has its own jurisdiction and is entirely separate from Argyll County Council. It is a youngish town. In 1788 the Fishery Board decided to develop the herring industry by building three new ports at Oban, Ullapool (Wester Ross) and Tobermory. As herring ports they unfortunately all collapsed, due partly to mismanagement, but more particularly to the fact that the fish seemed to alter course, migrating to different waters. They were expensive failures. However, today, Tobermory is a prosperous little place, with the added excitement of meeting the mail steamer in each day.

'Tobermory' means 'Mary's Well'; '*Tobar*', the Gaelic for 'well', and '*Muire*' for the Virgin Mary. A legend maybe, but then you come to a legend just as the steamer enters the Sound of Mull near Duart Castle, and on the starboard side pass a rock in the middle of the sea, known as 'Lady's Rock'. MacLean of Duart was supposed to have marooned his wife on that rock, leaving her to drown; but it was said that a galley belonging to her family came and rescued her; and thereafter MacLean's brother-in-law called on him at his Edinburgh home and murdered him as he slept. Tobermory is a place of beauty, well wooded, and Spanish gold lies deep in its harbour !

I had arrived at Aros—pronounced 'Aa-ross'.

The family I knew had plenty of money, for apart from this summer residence they had a big house on the Clyde, and 'father' was in the shipbuilding industry. They had a son and daughter, both in their 30's; the son, Iain, was intending to go abroad; the daughter, Jean, was a capable girl who had a musical turn of mind. It was a free-and-easy household, and we really did nothing but laze about admiring the view, and breathing in the bracing tonic of the Mull air. They had a small car which they permanently kept in Mull; Father leaving his Bentley at home; and we went various little trips round Mull. But they were not 'car-minded' as I was, and it generally seemed too much bother to take the car out.

Food was good and plentiful ; and about twice a week we would slip into Tobermory for essentials. The wine was also in liberal supply from the cellar down below the kitchen floor. It was a real change for me, as I had never been in Mull before ; and the evenings passed pleasantly in reading and Jean playing the piano. After some weeks Father had a sudden call to Glasgow, and Mother, Jean and Iain decided to go too. They pressed me to stay on for the remaining summer, and then lock up the whole place, leaving the keys with the police at Tobermory ; and above all, 'be sure to empty the water from the car radiator for the winter, and wrap the engine up well with blankets, rugs and coal bags !'

They left on the mail steamer from Tobermory ; and so did I, for I thought it wiser to get my own car over from Oban, and tour Mull, than use someone else's. I said goodbye to them at Oban railway station, their last words being 'and remember to drain the car', collected my own small Renault Caravelle, and then took the afternoon steamer back to Mull ; settled myself in at the 'big hoose' (for I was well able to cook and look after myself) and felt I was a real millionaire of leisure, in such a mansion and amidst such pleasant surroundings.

After a day or so, and seeing to all there was to be seen to in the house (there were no animals or livestock fortunately), I felt I would have a leisurely look round and go into Tobermory for a nice lunch at the big hotel there, high up above the harbour —the Western Isles Hotel—a lovely spot, delightfully situated in its own grounds, commanding an impressive view ; in fact I would say it has the finest site in the Hebrides. The hotel has every modern comfort, spacious lounge and sun parlour ; cocktail bar and the whole building centrally heated and managed by a friendly and charming couple whom I got to know very well later on. Moreover, the cuisine harmonised with the atmosphere —and I am more than partial to food. It is really a beautiful hotel in every respect ; 'true beauty dwells in deep retreats, whose veil is unremoved'.

Mull is spoken of in a Gaelic song as being 'of isles the fairest, the first and rarest of ocean gems', and it is really true.

I enjoyed being alone and wandering along Tobermory's nice

esplanade, gazing in at the shop windows, and invariably I returned back 'home' to Aros, refreshed and feeling very much at ease. I made these frequent excursions usually at the time the *Claymore* berthed on its way back to Oban about 4 o'clock on Mondays, Wednesdays and Fridays ; the locals usually turning out then to have a look at the strangers, and let you do the same to them! Gradually I became known to all and sundry. As a 'foreigner' I was slowly—very slowly—obtaining Mulleach citizenship!

Some days I would take a walk from the house, down through the village on to the main road and then back again ; there was seldom anyone about. I felt I was in one of the Isles of Youth— a place where one could do as one pleased ; rest and recapture the music and the breath of youth. I knew full well that my beloved Gairloch and district was unsurpassable in its beauty, its peaceful-ness and its great and friendly people ; the dim blue of its moun-tains, the mirror-surface of its many islet-studded lochs, the green glens and the sheen-white sands of land-locked bays—the Paradise that was to be ; but this was an island, and there seems to be a different 'touch' about an island than elsewhere, for islands appear to have a special charm and fascination of their own. Looking out and across from Mull, and seeing so many different other islands dotted in the setting sun, they likened themselves to enchanted isles ; isles of peace, solitude and freedom.

The morning light seemed to bring them all up from the sea, breaking the mist and summer haze like the prows of great ships coming in out of the ocean ; sun, sea, and sky, slash and girdle them with colours and forms for ever melting, changing and re-forming, as every whisper and wisp of wind, tide and cloud also changed.

In such isles the burdens of responsibility, obligation and compulsion seem to be left behind ; and the eye and heart are satisfied. Looking out and across at the Hebrides—the long chain of the Hebrides—one's mind conjures up pictures of the warriors ; the heroes and the heroines of ancient days. Their valour and grace, their kindness and sorrow are now changed to music—the music in the sounding shores, or in the cry of a bird or a voice of the burns, or in the droning of bees in the heather. For it must be remembered these distant isles were, in fact, the southern isles of the Norsemen. Every loch and creek has seen the arrival of the pillaging Vikings of old ; and on every headland and shore the Highlanders—ancestors of the very people with the same names as today—once stood to give them a welcome of steel.

Looking out from 'my' island, and 'my' White House—temporary though it was—one could see the blue peat smoke rising from some croft chimney ; the indigo and foam of the Atlantic ; the endless sands on countless isles ; the white clustered hamlets . . . the far purple promise of the Outer Isles ; and the purple-hued heights of Mull, capped by wisps of white clouds.

On clear days, and with a favourable gentle wind, the Cuillins of Skye appeared in all their glory, towering up on the horizon. And in the mentioning of that great romantic island (which I can also clearly see each day from my Gairloch home), my mind always turns to Flora Macdonald and Prince Charlie—the heroine of the '45 who was the most illustrious woman the Highlands and Islands have produced. She was born in South Uist in the spring of 1722, and reared at Milton there, of which her father was tacksman (gentleman farmer). She was born into a family whose claim to high rank could be established both on the male and on the female side. Through her father she derived her descent from the Chiefs of Clanranald and from the House of Dunnyveg in Kintyre ; whilst on her mother's side she had a pedigree stretching back to the Chiefs of Sleat. She was thus a genuine daughter of the lordly and aristocratic Macdonald House of the Isles, founded by the great and mighty Somerled, known to history as *Rex Insularum*. Flora was also descended from the House of Argyll, her great-grandmother—on her father's side—having been Agnes, daughter of Colin, Earl of Argyll. Through the Argyll family she could trace her descent to the Scottish Royal House of Robert II, as well as through her Macdonald line ; her ancestor John, 1st Lord of the Isles, having married the Princess Margaret, daughter of Robert II.

Thus, Flora Macdonald was not a mere peasant girl, as is often alleged by many writers, but was one who had the best blood in Scotland—that of the Lords of the Isles, the Earls of Argyll and the Kings of Scotland—mingling in her veins.

Although being English, I am genuinely moved in reading all about Flora Macdonald ; there is never a day, in looking out of my Gairloch house and seeing Skye and the Cuillins so clearly, but that I couple the sight with 'Flora'. She died, after a lingering illness, on 4th March 1790, aged 68 years, at Peinduin ; and I call to mind the beautiful words inscribed over her grave at Kilmuir—in the northern tip of Skye—namely, 'Her name will be mentioned in history ; and if courage and fidelity be virtues, mentioned with honour'. Her husband, Allan Macdonald, whom she married at Armadale (in Sleat, Skye, on 6th November 1750), died two years later, on 20th September 1792 ; and he too is buried with Flora in the Kingsburgh burial place in Kilmuir. On the Iona cross erected in 1880 (to replace the original one erected on 9th November 1871, and which was blown down and broken to fragments during a storm in December 1873) over Flora's grave at Kilmuir, it is said she died at Kingsburgh, Skye. But this is not correct, for, as I have said, she died at Peinduin, which was a small crofthouse (now in ruins) about 1½ miles north of Kingsburgh House, just over the river Hinnisdal, which flows into Loch Snizort Beag, where it joins Loch Snizort. It would be in those days about 4½ miles south of Uig.

There is a statue to her on Castle Hill, Inverness, the capital of the Highlands, which has the following Gaelic inscription under her name :

FHAD'S A DH'FHASAS ; FLURAIR MACHAIR ; MAIRIDH
CLIU NA ; H-AINNIR CHAOIMH ;

followed by the English inscription, viz. :

As long as a flower grows on a field
So long will the fame of the maiden endure.

Very touching ; very sweet indeed.

Slanderous stories have been invented and circulated by many writers regarding the Prince's relations with his rescuer, Flora ; but these are not worthy of consideration. I have read through authentic data—particularly *The Truth about Flora Macdonald* (out of print now), by the Rev. Donald Mackinnon, D.Litt., of Portree, and later of the Free Church Manse, Kennoway, Fife (the greatest authority on Flora Macdonald)—and there is not the slightest foundation for thinking or assuming that any 'love' entered into their two lives. The whole episode in which they were together lasted less than two days—from a Friday to a Sunday afternoon ; and the whole of their association was in the presence of several others. It was a perilous enterprise she was engaged in, solely and wholly ; and for which she will always and truthfully be remembered. I am also indebted to Mr. Reginald H. Macdonald of Kingsburgh, O.B.E., of Pittsburgh, Pennsylvania, U.S.A., who was a great-great-grandson of Flora Macdonald, for his great work on *The House of Macdonald of Kingsburgh and Castle Camus* (Skye), in his compilation of the genealogy of the Macdonalds dating back to Somerled Rex Insularum, who was wellnigh an independent King and Thane of Argyll, and who founded the Celtic Lordship of the Isles. Somerled married in 1140 Ragnhildis, daughter of Olave the Red, Norwegian King of Man and the Isles, and from that marriage derives, broadly, the Clan Donald and directly the Kingsburgh family. Somerled was treacherously murdered in his tent in 1164 by an emissary of King Malcolm IV just before the Battle of Renfrew was joined, but his family suffered no particular diminution of its power after his death and remained in possession of the vast territories he had won.

Aye, the Cuillins—with their absolute and utter detachment—bring back memories.

> The Cuillins stand silent ; and so,
> As one wanders alone on the shore,
> One thinks of the old MacLeod motto,
> 'Hold Fast' ; but the Cuillins say more.
>
> Entranced, you behold and recall,
> They were formed in the timeless past ;
> A message so simple for all,
> Endure, Fight on, and Hold Fast.

So I mused ; and I had plenty of spare time to muse.

During one of my walks I passed a neat little cream-coloured croft cottage at the end of the hamlet, and as I wanted a few fresh eggs, I ventured through the big white-painted gate, up the path lined with flowers to the front door, hoping there would be no vicious dog bounding out to sample me. I saw two or three cats stretched out, sunning themselves—but fortunately no dog.

The door was open ; I knocked, and waited. No reply, so I went round to the back where I saw a byre and henhouse, and my footsteps on the gravel path brought forth a young, and obviously Highland lass, who gave me a beautiful smile with an equally sweet 'good morning', saying, 'Is there anything I can do for you ?' At the same time excusing herself by saying she was

cleaning out the byre, hence her dirty wellington boots, old
sweater and 'working skirt'!

I was slightly taken aback by her genial complaisance, affabil-
ity and sweetness, not so common in a Highland village—for
although they 'ooze' with hospitality beyond all measure, they
are all characteristically very backward in unbridling their emotions. I explained where I was from—'the big hoose'—who I
was, and that I was staying at The White House as the owners
had suddenly gone back to town, and I wondered if I could have
a few eggs. 'Of course,' she said, 'I can always let you have some
eggs.' 'And are the lairds away for long ?' 'Yes,' I said, 'I don't
think they will be back this summer ; they've left the house in
my charge until the autumn, when I'm locking up and depositing
the keys with the police, for I must then get on my way to Gairloch in Ross-shire, where I'm building a "dream house".' 'Oh,
but how nice,' she said, 'Gairloch of all places. And are you
living all alone in that big house ?' 'Yes, all alone,' I said, 'but
I'm managing fine and finding a lot to interest me, for I haven't
been in Mull before and am thinking of writing a book on the
island and islands generally—a sort of companion to another one
that has just been published.' 'Oh, how very interesting,' she
replied, and continuing, she said, 'If you're wanting any local
knowledge, I am sure I could help you with a few items, for I know
Mull fairly well, since we have been living here for a few years.'
'We ?' I said. 'Yes ; my mother, who is a semi-invalid, and
brother Colin ; he works in the forestry department ; out most
of the day, and when he gets back he's in need of a good hot meal ;
so, all things considered, I'm kept busy.' 'Yes, you surely are.
You won't have much spare time ?' With that she laughed—an
infectious laugh, 'Oh, no ; there's always plenty to do even on a
wee croft, with a cow and a few hens—apart from the cats you see
around'—and which had followed on my heels. Sometimes, however, she told me, she went along to help out Mrs. Macphie at the
post office when she wanted a day off to go to Oban for messages.

After more pleasantries I came away with a dozen warm,
newly-laid eggs, saying I would look in again one morning, if I
might, when she was not so busy and when I was wanting more
eggs. 'And milk,' she cried out. 'I can always let you have a pint
of milk.' Thanking her very much, I went down the path, and
in closing the gate behind me—marked 'Keep shut'—saw she was

still smiling at me from the front door, and shyly waving goodbye.

Such a nice girl, I murmured to myself as I wended my way back ; so pleasant, and she seemed so happy to see me and chat. Yes, a very nice girl! I wondered who they were ; what her mother and brother were like ; if she had any particular boy friend. She certainly wasn't engaged or married, for she was wearing no ring—unless she had taken it off during 'working hours'. Thus did I mumble to myself, saying, 'Yes, I must certainly call again ; yes, sir !'

Back home, and after a nice tea and two of the fresh eggs, I sat and lazed before a fire during the evening, for it had started to rain—straight-up-and-down Highland rain—switched on the standard lamp and took up a book. But am afraid I read very little, for my mind kept wandering back to the wee croft ; and the wee lassie. I thought she would be about forty-ish or so ; a lovely, yes, a lovely complexion and hazel eyes, and 'very fair to look upon' ; a nice cuddly, curvaceous figure to be sure—and did not philosopher John Ruskin say a hundred years ago, 'A curve is more beautiful than a straight line'? . . . Yes, she was very nice ; very sweet indeed ; the sort of sweetness I felt I would like to wake up with one morning—every morning in fact—married to such an ideal wife ; for there was no doubt she must be practical in every way, having a semi-invalid mother, and a brother away all day, and only her to do the cooking and the chores, and looking after the croft ; bringing in the cow at nights to milk, feeding the hens and preparing their meal, lifting potatoes, planting potatoes, to say nothing of all the other vege-tables that go with a crofting life. Yes, a fine girl—or woman, I should say, and again I said to myself 'so sweet'. Yes, I think I could 'fall for her' as I drowsily thought over it all. She seemed a strong girl too ; she needed to be, with so much on her hands ; and I thought of the quotation, 'Out of the strong came forth sweetness'. The saying was quite apt.

I wanted to call again next day, but believed *that* would be rather *too* pointed ; *too* impetuous, or *too* forward mayhap ? So I left it for a few days ; and then, plucking up courage, I called again. She came to the front door, and smilingly I said I hadn't come for any more eggs just yet! In fact I had come for nothing really, but if she was not too busy I would like to have a chat on general croft life, so as to keep me on the right lines for my book. Her face lit up : 'Come in,' she said, 'I'm not too busy and you can meet Mother.' And I gladly entered, bending my head low under the front door beam. Mother greeted me with an equally warm, affectionate smile, and said Fiona, her daughter, had told her I had called the other day. 'Fiona,' I said, 'that's a very nice name ; sort of Gaelic for "Flora" ; and it has a touch of Iona about it also ?' 'Yes, indeed,' said Mother ; 'well, come and sit by the fireside ; we always welcome strangers to our humble abode, and since Fiona tells me you are living at the big house all alone, you must surely be lonely ?' 'Yes, it is a bit quiet, but I'm used to that,' I replied. 'I would take a cup of tea ?' 'Yes, thank you, that would be nice,' I said, 'for I can take tea any time of the day.' 'And Fiona,' she called, 'get out some cake and shortbread for Mr. ?' 'Bee Jay,' I said, 'is the name most of my friends call me, and I'd like you to call me the same, if you will.' 'Bee Jay ?' said Mother (and Fiona too) 'that's an odd name ?' 'Not really, for it embodies part of my initials,' I replied ; 'and one that I was universally known by in Ceylon, where I was for nearly twenty-five years ; and the nickname or pen-name has stuck with me all these years.' 'Oh, indeed,' she said.

Fiona made the tea quickly (for the kettle, spouting steam, was on the gleaming hob, as it generally is in these cottages), cut the cake and brought in treacle scones and shortbread, butter and home-made jam ; and all three of us sat around the kitchen fire. It was very homely ; they were very charming and I loved it all (and subsequently, as the years passed, I can truthfully, and from the depth of my heart, say that never in my life had I met such a dear, sweet old Highland woman as Fiona's mother ; in fact they were a wonderfully closely-knitted family—the greatest I had ever known ; their hospitality and their thoughtfulness knew no bounds. Truly, they were God's own people).

Afraid of outstaying my welcome, in about an hour I said I must be getting along home ; but said I really would like to come along one evening and meet Colin—if I would not be intruding. 'Certainly you must,' they both said, 'any time you will be welcome ; and you'll stay for supper, which we generally have about 7 o'clock.'

Thanking them in my best party manner, it was arranged I would go along 'first Saturday', for Colin would be home early that day, and there would be no rush as to his meal, etcetera. As this was Thursday, there were only two more days before I would be driving up in my car to Croft Cottage ; driving on velvet, so to speak.

I left then, Fiona seeing me down to the gate, and saying, 'You must tell us of your life abroad next time' ; and I felt an 'inglowing-ness' in me (which I hoped she felt too)—a feeling of being welcomed in a real cosy home with genuine folk around ; and who appeared to be more than cheered by the likes of me dropping in. That I felt honoured thereby was an understatement ; I felt proud they should have been so kindly disposed to me, a stranger—in fact a foreigner !

Yes, there was no doubt about it, she was sweet—and in that respect, the image of her mother. Theirs was the life that appealed to me—not the croft-life of course, but a care-free life away from the bustle, din and nerve-wracking city life, and city crowds ; a life lived in an atmosphere of peaceful reality—in fact a life I was carefully planning out at my own Gairloch domain in Wester Ross, and which would soon 'come to pass', and which, I prayed, would be the end of the rainbow, *my* rainbow, *my* happiness with one beside me, loving and sweet, and living always and ever for each other. I always felt there is nothing more lovely in life than the union of two people whose love for one another grows through the years from the small acorn of passion into a great-rooted tree. I was wondering, under the 'household circumstances', if Fiona would ever think of marrying—and perhaps marrying me ? They were, I subsequently gathered, members of the Free Kirk. I was naturally brought up in the Church of England style. But that did not present any obstacle in the least degree ; whatever religion we belong to, we are all climbing up different sides of the same mountain. And one day, we all arrive at the top.

Little did I know, as I crossed over to Mull, that my 'search' *was* coming to a close.

Saturday came in no time, and I drove up a little before 7 o'clock, parking the car on the verge. Fiona came running out to say there was no need to keep my lights on, for the police-sergeant was never around on Saturdays ; he was too busy keeping watch (and order) on the public bars of Tobermory—or in having a few 'haufs' himself !

On coming into the parlour, and after greeting Mother, I was introduced to Colin ; 'My big brother', as Fiona called him. He was certainly well built and of good physique ; typically the forest man who, in felling trees, would shout stentoriously, 'T–I–M–B–E–R !' as it toppled to the ground. He was quite amused at my telling him that. He said he didn't do any 'felling', but was more or less concerned with the planting, general observations and surveys, reporting back to the Forestry Commission, and was hoping one day to get a job in head office on the mainland. He had a small car which took him all over the island in his work, supervising and checking up. We talked a while about different species of wood abroad, and that I was intending to have all my ceilings at my Gairloch home lined with obeche wood from Nigeria.

We sat down to a spotless table, and after grace being said, Mother carved the roast chicken, which was served with sausages, haggis, bread sauce, roast potatoes and cauliflower ; all beautifully done, and of course I was not slow in complimenting the cook, to wit, Fiona! 'But,' said Mother, 'I cook as well, you know! Though I'm not as nimble as of yore, I still manage to hobble around and prepare meals at times.' It was 'high tea' really, and therefore no soup ; just the chicken, etc., bread and butter, tea, followed by newly-baked pancakes and warm flowery scones you wanted to cuddle ; oatcake, shortbread and cake. (I don't think I've forgotten anything!) And what could not be accommodated on the table was put on the sideboard. Oh, yes, and biscuits and cheese if you were still peckish! Surely Scotland is the best place to take an appetite ; you are thought to be off-colour should you refuse a second helping !

I loved the haggis with the chicken ; it seemed to add a special degree of relish to it. 'The' haggis, as it is generally termed in Scotland, is a dish one seldom comes across south of the border ; many restaurants or hotels in England would look at you in dismay if you said, 'What! no haggis with the chicken ?' If you look up your cookery book it is doubtful if you will ever see the recipe for haggis, unless you look up the index and find the chapter 'Cooking for the Courageous'. And perhaps at this point I had better explain details of the makings of a haggis ; the dish that someone said contributed to the decline and fall of the Roman Empire! In this respect I do believe some English folk

think haggis is a kind of rugged Highland animal, or else the
particular name given to the strong, dour, bearded, six-foot,
hairy-kneed Highlanders found living in some far region of northern Scotland—either that, or a boy's name : Hamish, Haggis or
such-like. Here is a good Highland recipe given me, when later
on I became to know Fiona's mother better :

> 1 sheep's heart
> ½ lb. sheep's liver
> ½ lb. chopped suet
> ½ lb. oatmeal
> 2 chopped onions
> ½ pint soup stock
> Teaspoonful of salt and pepper to season.

Briefly, you wash and boil the heart and liver for a while ;
then mince it finely, put everything into a large bowl covered
over with greaseproof paper. Put into a large enough pan and
steam for two or three hours until the mixture is dryish and
crumbly. Serve with swedes and mashed potatoes.

That is all there is to it ! and, believe me, you'll be wanting
second helpings. At public functions in Scotland in particular,
the haggis comes into prominence on Burns's night and St.
Andrew's night—25th January and 30th November respectively.
But whatever night, or nights, the haggis is the same ; its dress
does not alter ; it just comes out wrapped up in its own lining of
a sheep's stomach !

It is served hot, steaming hot, and eaten with the usual knife
and fork, not by brandishing a claymore or a skean-dhu at it, for
a haggis is a temperamental, exclusive morsel and quick to sense
if you are acquaint with 'himself, himself' ; just as a horse can
judge if it has a novice astride its saddle. And a tot of whisky
poured over it, and you can then call the Lord-Lieutenant of Mull
your uncle ! Take courage in both hands and make a hearty meal
of it, for a haggis respects courage. Haggis, *the* haggis, ranks as a
V.I.P.—a Very Important Pudding ; for did not Rabbie Burns
term it 'Great Chieftain o' the puddin' race' ? And *that* turned
its head and it became famous overnight.

I heard of a true case of a haggis being ordered from Scotland
by an Ontario Burns Club and being interned by the Canadian
Agriculture Department ; the official reason given being that the
haggis arrived without the government seal, which every parcel

of imported meat must have. Too bad? And yet another case, this time from Australia to a Scots lassie there, never reached its destination. A letter from the Adelaide Customs said it was not allowed into Australia, and consequently it was in quarantine, would be confiscated and destroyed! A similarly-worded letter was sent her from the Health Department for Animals, 'Seized and to be destroyed'! So English folk who thought, and think, a haggis is an animal are not alone surely?

If it's 'a meal you want, then it's haggis you want' is a bright and snappy slogan, apart from its vitamin contents or its basic formula. Not only have you to take into account its 'constituency', but one needs consider the method of approach to obtain its topmost value, for have I not already said, the haggis is a temperamental subject; a delicate bite, peculiar to its own. To the native Scot the haggis is akin to porridge. He has been happily brought into this world, and subsequently reared in this land, on these two fundamental dishes, which many term as succulent; and those who may look askance at the dish, or even scorn it, do so in doubtless envy? As for myself, I would say 'A haggis a day keeps the doctor away!'

Och aye; the snow is on the bens, the haggis is on the boil, and the hunter home from the hills. At times it rains; but who cares, for a rainbow appears in the heavens and curves all over the village and the bay beyond, its colours reflected in the sky and on the snow-capped peaks of Mull and the Cuillins; a wonderful background 'sweeping down to the sea', far more majestic than those we can see in Ireland from Mull—'the mountains of Mourne that sweep down to the sea'.

Yes, the haggis is in Dan the butcher's shop, and venison too, dressed, looking tempting to buy; and a nice juicy trout looks up at you from its cold, cold slab—with cod-like eyes; and one murmurs *Slàinte Mhath*; a most appropriate murmur!

So much for the haggis interlude!

After this 'banquet' of a supper at Croft Cottage, we sat beside the peat fire and I talked to them of Ceylon, the tropics, and life abroad in general, after I had insisted on helping Fiona to clear the table. I wanted to help in the washing up, but that was 'verboten', 'taboo', 'not done'; and so on! She would attend to that later, but I made it understood that the next time I came

I *would* be allowed to help her in the kitchen ; and she said, 'very well then, next time!'

They told me of their reasons for being in Mull. It appeared Mother was born and brought up in Wester Ross, overlooking beautiful Gruinard Bay, married, and later on in life, and the family growing up, they all came over to Mull as her husband got work as chauffeur and general handyman in one of the big houses on the west side looking across to Ulva, a tiny island barely a mile off-shore. In the summer, as the laird had a yacht, he also acted as cook on board during their short cruises round the Western isles. He retired and bought this wee croft to earn a little more before intending to go back to Ross-shire ; but unfortunately he passed away before that dream was realised. The family grew up ; they had had another son Iain, Mother said, but he was 'lost at sea' during the Second World War whilst working on a minesweeper. Fiona did a little nursing—as the great majority of Highland girls do—and Colin became 'tree-minded'. After the war, Fiona gave up her nursing career to look after her mother and the croft ; and Colin was fortunate enough to secure the job in Mull. They had now resigned themselves to living the rest of their lives in Mull, and had got a tenant for the Ross-shire croft. They were, of course, keenly interested in my living permanently at Gairloch (not far from Gruinard)—the loveliest place in the whole of the Highlands, they said ; and Fiona commented that when that *did* come to pass, I would not be coming back to Mull again ? And I think she said that with a faint touch of sadness in her voice. I said, 'No, I don't suppose I will, once I get my dream house finished, for I'll have lots to do, much as though I will miss you all here in Mull' ; but I said, 'One never knows, one cannot tell, what fates the gods hold in their spacious laps.' To that they all murmured 'true, very true'. However, I told them I should not be going for several months ; and when I was permanently in residence there, should any of them come and visit the 'old haunts', they would always find the front-door key under a stone near the lily pond ; and should I happen to be out, then I said, 'Just walk right in ; put on the kettle and the tea caddy will be near by, and make yourselves at home, and await my return !' They laughed and said they'd take me at my word.

Towards the end of the evening and after late tea and cake, I turned to Fiona, saying perhaps she would like to come out with me in the car some odd days and show me around and give me the 'gen' on certain items and legends connected with the island that I would like to know. She said she'd be very pleased and happy to do so, 'though I don't know everything associated with Mull, but I'll do my best!'

Having bravely got so far, and all being very much at home, I suggested as a change for Mother (who did not go out much) if they would like me to collect them one evening in the car and for us to have a dinner at the Tobermory Western Isles Hotel? 'Oh! that would be lovely,' but Mother said, 'We'll see; for you know, Mr. Bee Jay, I really stay indoors most evenings; but Colin and Fiona could easily go without me.'

So that was agreed; I would call round the following Saturday ('Saturday first') about 6 p.m. and pick them all up; and if Mother did not feel like joining in, then Fiona and Colin would come.

I said goodbye about 10 o'clock, thanking them profusely for the grand homely evening I had spent in their midst, and saying I would drop in one morning the following week in advance of the Saturday, just—with a twinkle in my eye—to see if they were still alive and breathing! 'That would be fine,' said Fiona; and she saw me to the gate. I felt a burning desire to linger, or to ask her if she would like a run to the outskirts of Tobermory (two miles) and back; but thought I had better not push my wares too forcibly!

I dropped in one morning the next week to see how everyone was, and as usual was received with smiles of welcome, together with the time-honoured cup of tea and buttered scones.

Saturday came round; and dressing myself up in a lounge suit, discarding the usual 'fisherman's' jersey I always wore during the week, and which was so warm and serviceable, I called round on the dot of 6 o'clock. Mother said I must excuse her not joining us, for she felt—as she put it—a bit out of things, going to an hotel for dinner. 'Oh! dear me, no; *do* come,' I maintained; but she preferred to stay at home that night; so in the end, Fiona and Colin hopped into the car, and we sped away; Fiona sitting with me in the front seat.

Arriving at the hotel, Colin and I had an apéritif, Fiona saying she really didn't take cocktails, but instead had an orange juice.

It was a nice meal—the 'Western Isles' can always be relied upon for a good tasty fare ; much cross-chat mingled with laughs, then coffee in the lounge, and after spending a grand evening we left, reaching home about 10.30 p.m. It was still comparatively light, for it was only early July, and the moon was high. Stopping at the gate they asked me to come in, but I said it was late enough and I would be getting along ; so Colin bade me goodnight and went to put his car into the lean-to garage for the night. Fiona and I stood around, she saying what a treat it was to have had an evening out ; and myself saying it was an added joy to me having such a lovely person beside me. I had thoroughly enjoyed myself, I said, and looking at me with eager eyes she answered 'Did you really ?' 'Yes,' and drawing nearer and taking her hand to say goodnight, I bent forward and said, 'May I kiss you good-night for making my evening so wonderful, so complete ? . . .' She did not answer ; there was no need to answer ; we kissed, and at that moment we both knew—in the unspoken language of lovers—that we had fallen in love.

It was all so touching ; so sudden ; it was a feeling and a love, far, far different from tropical splendour, or the land of the Pharaohs. Of that, there was no question. It was not that we were young and carried away, for we were both of a mature age and sensible.

It had come to pass—and in Mull of all places.

'Goodnight, darling.' 'Goodnight, dear,' she said, 'and I'll look forward to seeing you soon' ; and with that I revved up the car, saying I would be along tomorrow, and on to the White House.

There is truly one golden, and lasting rule, in winning each other's love : namely to sink oneself into each other's heart and to mould oneself to the one by whom you would wish to be loved ; and this I pledged myself to do ; and I prayed when I got home that this might be—or rather it *would* be—the end of the rainbow, and that surely after all the years of search there could be no tragedy forthcoming at this time, and at this late hour in life, lurking around the corner or coming out of the skies ?

Yes, love is a 'many splendoured thing' : real love. And when back home and in bed, I tossed and tossed, thinking always of Fiona ; 'my Fiona '. . . . And again and again I found myself

G

saying how sweet she was. A nameless grace waved in her raven tresses, and over her softly lightened face I could sense her thoughts were serenely and sweetly expressed ; her smile that had such a winning manner ; soft, calm and eloquent, telling of days spent in goodness and peace ; and above all a heart that was golden and true.

Of course, I called the next day and indeed every day ; and my visits and presence were more than welcome. I was now looked upon as one of the family ; and how honoured—deeply honoured—I felt. I literally lived for each day ; I was living a new life. A stranger in a strange land—'and YE took me in'.

These truly were halcyon days.

'He leadeth me the quiet waters by ; my soul He doth restore again.'

My horizon was widened. Love was the key that had unlocked the door of my heart again.

CHAPTER 12

HALCYON DAYS IN MULL

IT was getting near the end of July ; and towards the middle of September I needed to think of going off up to Gairloch to see the various men working at my house, for they were planning to start work in earnest then. It would take six months to finish everything off and they would have to work all through the wintry months—with flood-lights, I imagined!

I felt I must get busy on seeing all round Mull and Iona ; and so for two or three days of the week Fiona joined me in the car on our excursions—business excursions I told her! And she would say, smilingly, showing the dimple in her cheek, 'but of course!' She would leave things all prepared and at hand for her mother to cook and get her meals, and if we got back home about 7 o'clock she would be ready to prepare Colin's meal ; and I would always stay on, enjoying the evening supper with them, for have I not already said I was looked upon as one of themselves ?—one of the family, cats and all!

I suggested we first 'did' Tobermory, and work round the island from the capital. The roads are good in Mull, but narrow, and for the most part their width does not allow two cars to pass unless it be at the 'passing places', which are frequent and clearly marked. This is a peculiarity of the roads up in the Highlands. And, let it be said, these 'passing places' are what their name implies—for 'passing' not for 'parking' or admiring the view, or over-night caravanning. They in fact take the 'wrinkles' out of the many bends.

There is an attractive walk from Tobermory along the coast to the lighthouse Rudha nan Gall, and beyond to 'Bloody Bay', an historic spot which got its name about 1480. In view of the inaccessibility of Mull, the government took little heed of what was going on amidst the chiefs there. Old John of Islay—an island south of Mull and adjoining Jura—wished to be known as the Lord of the Isles, and by one means and another the government granted him his title. He had an undutiful son, named Angus, who disapproved of his father's actions, and in due course waged war against him. His ships were commanded by Hector MacLean of Duart Castle. There was a sea battle, and the Mac-Leans beached their boats in the bay, and hid in a cave near by. They were soon discovered by their enemies, who built a fire at the mouth of the cave, and it is recorded that none of the party survived. But in less than fifteen years after this battle at 'Bloody Bay', the renowned days of the Lords of the Isles ended.

We did the walk in the morning; and after lunch at the hotel, as we sat having coffee in the sun lounge overlooking Tobermory's wonderful bay, I asked Fiona to tell me all she knew about the Spanish treasure—the Tobermory treasure—lying almost beneath our feet, the tale or legend of the gold of the *Almiranta de Florencia*, which for the past four centuries no one so far has apparently been able to find. 'Tell me the fairy story, Fiona'— and she did.

Many are the tales, she said, which have been handed down through succeeding generations; but this is the generally accepted one, Stanley, she said, and you can take it or leave it!

In short, it was in Tobermory Bay that this Spanish ship was sunk in 1588, taking with her a vast treasure of gold.

The *Florencia* was a Spanish galleon which set sail with the Armada to conquer England. Drake was playing bowls on Plymouth Hoe! She was a big ship and belonged to the Portuguese squadron; and she had much gold aboard. After the encounter in the English Channel (Drake having finished his game!) the captain of the *Florencia*, finding himself with a cumbersome ship in hostile waters and a strong wind, began to wonder if he would ever reach Spain again. He turned the ship about and went wherever the wind would take him. After many restless days he suddenly sighted an anchorage behind a small island. He brought his ship safely inside and dropped anchor; and though he did not know it at the time, it was Tobermory Bay. 'Go on, darling,' I said, 'I am all ears.' And looking around, and seeing no one looking, I gave her a kiss which I am sure we both 'treasured!'

The captain, Don Fareiga, sent a victualling party ashore, who came back with food and water for which they did not pay.

From such 'savages' as were in the place then, one simply 'took'. He reckoned, however, without MacLean of Duart, who in due course sent Donald Glas MacLean of Morvern to collect the dues; but Donald received scant courtesy; in fact Don Fareiga clapped him in chains. The captain was more concerned with the weather and his chances of getting back to Spain than with paying the natives for the food they had looted.

The day of calm came, and the *Florencia* spread her canvas and was on the point of leaving harbour, 'My, oh! my,' I said, 'this is becoming more and more exciting. I can hardly wait, Fiona.' 'Wait, darling, for I'm coming to the end.' 'Yes, I'm waiting dear, and you're telling me the story so vividly that it seems to have come down by word of mouth from generation to generation since days "when Homer was a boy".' 'Darling pet, wait,' she said.

MacLean, although in irons, managed to find a way through into the powder magazine and set fire to it. Before the *Florencia* cleared the bay and Calve Island, the explosion came and she foundered in the bay and was a total wreck. Whilst there is no doubt that a Spanish ship-of-war went to the bottom of Tobermory Bay, it is not known with absolute certainty if she carried any treasure.

Fiona said there are, of course, variations of this story: a gentleman—one Smollet, or Smallet, of Dumbarton, Dunbartonshire on the Clyde, is said to have blown the vessel up. There is still in existence, Fiona told me, a report made by Queen Elizabeth's ambassador in Edinburgh in 1588, to the effect that the ship was blown up by the 'wild and savage Irish in M'Lane's island of Mula!'

Many unsuccessful attempts have been made, she said, to recover the treasure supposedly lying deep in the harbour.

One Sackeverell, Governor of the Isle of Man, came in 1688 complete with a diving-bell! Here was a Manx statesman sitting at the bottom of Tobermory Bay in a leaky bell looking for Spanish gold! 'What a laugh,' I said, 'he'd go back home with his tail between his legs?' 'Oh!' said Fiona, 'but Manx cats have no tails!' How we both laughed at that!

Fifty years later, it seems another attempt was made, when a few guns and a little gold came to the surface. More expeditions came and went—none were successful. Always, something like a cannon-ball or a handful of coins or old metal ; but nothing else of value.

There are, she said, scholars who declare that it was not the *Florencia* but the *San Juan de Sicilia* that blew up ; and she was a small ship attached to the Levant squadron, and was carrying nothing but old iron.

Through the succeeding centuries, the family of Argyll (who in 1641 were granted the rights of salvaging the vessel by the King of Scotland) have sought to recover the treasure. The MacLeans of Duart challenged this right, but it still rests with the Duke of Argyll of Inveraray Castle.

It may be worthy of note that over ten years ago divers of the Royal Navy searched and confirmed the fact that there is a wreck lying on the sea-bed not far from the pier. But what wreck ? There are many wrecks lying on the bottom of the sea in Tobermory Bay ; and by this time they will be well and truly sunk deeply in the mud and sand.

However, as Fiona had finished her fairy tale, I told her I'd still like to think that it *is* the good old *Florencia* lying down there, and that Donald Glas MacLean 'had done it'—the same as I said I would like to think there *is* a monster in Loch Ness! 'Oh, darling,' she said, as she clasped my hand and we kissed again, 'you *do* love romance!' 'Of course,' I answered, 'I do.' 'And you ?' 'But naturally I do, darling ; I'm a woman!'

I have remarked previously that Tobermory has a beautiful bay and esplanade, which we often walked along and made purchases from the many shops. There are three churches in Tobermory : St. Mary's Church of Scotland, the Free Church and the Baptist Church. There used to be another Kirk—the pre-union United Free Kirk—but the building has been converted into a knitwear factory. Some eighty years ago over 400 people attended the Gaelic service at the Free Kirk. Today, there is no Gaelic service, since there is practically no one speaking 'the Gaelic'.

So that was Tobermory ; and as we drove back home we fell more and more in love.

Our next trip was from Tobermory northwards, via Dervaig and Calgary, down part of the west coast line and across to Salen. Glengorm Castle at the northernmost point of the road, a few miles off the main Dervaig road, is barely one hundred years old, so may be considered modern, but a mile north-west of it the ruins of Dunara Castle are well worth seeing. Carrying on the main Dervaig road one passes the three Mishnish Lochs, quite a pleasant run. Dervaig itself is but a wee village at the head of Loch Cuin, and just before reaching the village itself one sees the Standing Stones said to be of Druidical origin. 'The Clearances' after the 1745 uprising, *Bliadna Thearlaich*' (Prince Charlie's year), hit Mull very hard, the people being ruthlessly evicted to make way for sheep, and were shipped off to Canada. I remark very freely on this aspect in *And It Came to Pass*, and also in Chapter 14. After Culloden—16th April 1746—a place of tragedy for countless Scots, and a day of futile sorrows echoing down the centuries (the story of Scotland's saddest defeat), there was much plunder and killing by the Duke of Cumberland (the 'bloody butcher' as history terms him). A reign of terror started to subdue the Highlands for ever. He was a veritable dictator, with one obsession, 'suppression'. Hundreds of thousands of clansmen were banished, that a degenerate lord might boast his sheep. Then the sheep went too. Such was the aftermath of 'Charlie's year'. Misery for the Highlands ; abject misery. Yet legend tells of Jacobite triumph in defeat. The Clan system in the old familiar sense—namely, a 'family', not a social hierarchy, was completely shattered by merciless measures. Glens were emptied by deportation or emigration. By the rigidly repressive Acts of 1746 and 1748 the old ties of clan kinship were cruelly broken. Henceforward until 1782, except by stealth, the tartan was unseen in the hills and glens, where before it had been the people's pride and joy.

It was savage legislation indeed, for, to the government, a Highlander was looked upon as a savage from the remote islands and northern regions of Scotland.

In 1782 the Duke of Montrose fought nobly for the repeal of the hated Disarming Act and was successful, but there was no immediate enthusiastic return to the tartan and the kilt. The old attachment to the Highland dress had died in a generation. The old patterns were forgotten ; so was the skill of making the dyes from the herbs on the hills. It was not until forty years later, towards the middle of the 1800's, that a romantic interest in Highland dress was reborn. During this melancholy period the oppressed Highlanders dourly and silently endured their wrongs, brooding upon the loss of their ancient heritage ; but powerless.

Gradually, and after the turn of the 19th century, Clan Societies grew up and multiplied in the New World and in Colonial Britain ; then slowly wherever Scotsmen dwelt, the sympathetic feeling of kinship was kindled and the tartan became symbolic, not of the Highlands alone, but of Scotland as a whole. And that is as we know it today.

A few miles further on, and before reaching Calgary, we took a side road to the sea to Croig, one of the old ports of Mull. It was from this port years ago that cattle were landed from the outer isles on their long trek south, walking and driven right down the entire length of Mull where they were then loaded on to boats at Grass Point, south of Duart Castle, *en route* to the island of Kerrera and thence over to the mainland near Oban ; and onwards, ever onwards (*vide* chapter on Oban). Returning to the main road again we came to Calgary and Calgary Bay, where in the old times the emigrant ships lay anchored in wait for the dispossessed crofters. Sad, sad times indeed. Calgary, Alberta, derives its name from the Calgary of Mull. The latter a village, the former a city.

The Calgary sands, washed by the Atlantic Ocean, are famous to visitors to Mull ; and the snowdrops there are usually well ahead in flower than elsewhere. Calgary Bay is wide and delightful, and near by at Caliach and Treshnish Points, sea birds haunt the cliffs. Across from here, one can see the rocky islands of Coll and Tiree ; and further on the horizon Rum, Eigg and Muck ; Canna and the Cuillins of Skye. Continuing the road southwards from Calgary, we skirt Loch Tuath, which delves deep into Mull ; and then via the north side of Loch-nan-Ceall, a haunt of seals, we soon reach Salen (pronounced ' *Sahlen*'). Thence back home, after having a nice afternoon tea at the small hotel there ; tea, buttered scones, and jam—as well as home-made cake.

I must mention that skirting Loch Tuath on high ground, there is a fine view of Ulva, Gometra and the Treshnish islands—with Staffa in the background. Ulva is a basalt island rising in terraces to over 1000 feet ; and it is privately owned, with a private ferry across to the mainland—just a stone's throw away. The MacArthurs, scarcely less celebrated than the great piping family of the MacCrimmons of Skye (*vide And It Came to Pass*), had their piping college on Ulva, then owned by the old family of MacQuarries. Until recently there was a fine Adam house on

Ulva, but unfortunately it was burned down. Halfway down the road bordering Loch Tuath there is Ballygown Bay where one can see a large Broch, or Fort, near the shore : the one and only kind in Mull, dating back to the 1st century A.D. Eas Fors, another mile further, is a fine waterfall seen each side of the bridge we cross over. And then, just before taking the road to Salen at the head of Loch-nan-Ceall, if one turns down towards the west road, one comes to Knock, and from Knock to Gribun. These 8 miles of detour by the southern shores of the loch are the wildest in Mull, for the road runs along and below cliffs, and in parts is carved out of the mountainside. Giant boulders hang poised over you as your car wends its way. There is a story that long ago some of these boulders crashed down and the avalanche wiped out a cottage and a young married couple ; in fact, the walls of the cottage with the boulder in its midst can be seen to this day. Another legend from Gribun is that told of MacKinnon's piper, who went with some men and a dog to explore the depths of a large cave which is entered at low water mark. The rest of the party remained on guard outside, the idea being they could then follow the sound of the pipes and plot the course of the cave. But no one ever returned from the cave and they were supposed to have been attacked by fairies ; although they spared the piper for music's sake ; but alas, before he could regain his path to the entrance, he 'gave up the ghost'. The dog, however, later on came up out of a hole many miles away. There was not a single hair on its body ! Burnt off it is said by the breath of some huge monster ! So the legend goes ; and some in Gribun to this day tell you if you listen carefully you can yet hear the sounds of music under the ground ! The cave has ever since been named MacKinnon's Cave. So says legend ; and so said Fiona !

Close to these Gribun Cliffs, just off-shore, is the island of Inch Kenneth (guarding, as it were, the entrance to Loch-nan-Ceall), called after Saint Kenneth, one of Saint Columba's disciples. There is an ancient chapel and a burial ground of the kings of Ireland and Scotland on this little island ; for when the funeral party was unable to reach Iona on account of storms and gales, they were laid to rest on Inch Kenneth island.

Our next itinerary was direct to Salen, down the coast to Craignure, Duart Castle and along Loch Spelve to Loch Buie on the south of the island.

Salen was founded by one General Lachlan MacQuarrie (1760–1825), the 'Father of Australia', a Mull man, who purchased the village, naming it 'Jarvis field' after his wife's maiden name. MacQuarrie was the first Governor-General of New South Wales ; and in later life came back to Mull and died there. His mausoleum is at Gruline, two miles inland from Salen. There are a number of legends in Salen connected with Saint Columba, who was said to have preached and worked there. Further along the main road, one comes to Glen Forsa Hotel, once the mansion house of the estate, but now owned by the Department of Agriculture and The Forestry Commission. Further still at Pennygown there is reputed to be a Fairy Mound, and by leaving a wish there, it will be granted by the so-called fairies. Near by is the ancient graveyard and chapel of Pennygown, where it is said MacLean of Duart and his wife practised black magic, with the result the chapel will be forever roofless ; and when Fiona and I passed it, sure enough there was no roof to be seen! The graves of both MacLean and his wife can be distinguished today. In the chapel can be seen a beautiful piece of carving on the broken part of a Celtic Cross, depicting the Virgin and Child.

Some eight miles south of Salen, at Garmony Bay, is a big rock, on which seals bask at low tide. Looking across from here to the shores of Morvern on the mainland, can be seen Ardtornish Castle. There appears to have been a chain of castles from Oban to Ardnamurchan Point for the purposes of flashing signals one to the other : thus Oban, Dunollie, Duart, Ardtornish, Aros, Morvern (Castle of the Dogs) and finally to Mingary Castle on Ardnamurchan.

From Salen to Craignure—eleven miles ; and from Craignure one gets a grand view of the mountains up the Lynn of Morven or as it is more commonly called Loch Linnhe, right up to Fort William with Ben Nevis in the background. Near the bay at Craignure is Java Lodge, where the islanders of Soay have been housed in nicely arranged flats and bungalows by the government. Soay is a small island sheltering in Loch Scavaig on the south-west of Skye, below the Cuillin Hills, and in 1953 these islanders petitioned the government to be taken off because the population had so declined they could not make a living. As I have said, they are all nicely housed near Craignure.

At Craignure the government are in the throes of building a

major new pier; and in December 1962 they announced that three vehicle ferries were to be built for the Western Isles, which will be a boon to the islanders and a boost to tourism; and these vessels are expected to be put into service in the summer of 1964.

The ferries are to be operated on charter to MacBraynes; and the contract—worth £1,500,000—has been given to an Aberdeen firm of boat builders. Each will carry up to 600 passengers and 52 cars, as well as livestock. The vessels are 230 feet long and will have a speed of $14\frac{1}{2}$ knots, and they are to be fitted with stabilisers and bow propellers for manœuvring at the piers. There will also be a cafeteria, smoke room and bar; and even sleeping accommodation for 52 passengers.

Concerning Mull, one of the ferries will operate between Oban and Craignure and across to Lochaline (Morvern); the other two, one on the Mallaig-Armadale (Skye) and Lochboisdale (South Uist) route; and one on the Uig (Skye), Lochmaddy (North Uist) and Tarbet (Harris) route.

The smaller islands of Rum, Eigg, Canna and Scalpay will be served by a smaller vessel, and it will ply from Mallaig. A major pier is also being constructed at Uig, and two others at Tarbet and Lochaline.

The result of all this will assuredly alter the whole economic position of the Western Isles; and life on the islands will be brightened and stimulated by these new services.

This car-linkage to Mull will have an astronomical effect. Tourists will be able to leap-frog from island to island with the greatest of ease and minimum of discomfort.

Hitherto, to get your car to these Hebridean isles, it meant a sling being placed under it and you beheld it being laboriously swung from the quayside on to the boat; and when it had safely landed, you gave a sigh of relief that nothing had been damaged 'in transit'—wharf to vessel. And of course only three or four cars could be taken on board, so you had to arrange the exact day you wanted your car to be shipped months in advance; and that was not always possible. No longer will one be afraid of being stranded or taken on to another island because the weather was too rough to allow the vessel to berth. The islander, too, will be happier; Donald's cattle will be driven right on to the ship's lift, instead of the poor beasts being man-handled and slung any old how into the hold. Stores and provisions will arrive on time.

The harassed, neglected, depopulated islands should flourish in this new brightness ; and not sit watching the sun go down. They needs be up and ready—hoteliers also—and take full advantage of the great influx that will certainly come along. Tourists don't look for four- or five-star luxury hotels amongst the Highlands ; but more for homely food and homely comforts ; with FÀILTE (welcome) written on the mat, or on the farmyard gates.

But of course along with all this comes the need for adequate car-parking facilities and the widening of roads to cope with the extra traffic. These two points, unless resolved at once, will be the weak links in what will be a great new traffic chain.

From Craignure we come to Duart : Duart Castle, which is the grimmest castle in Scotland ; ancestral home of that proud and powerful island family—the MacLeans of Duart. For many years Duart Castle was in ruins. By 1913 it was restored and lived in by the then 26th chief of the clan, Sir Fitzroy MacLean—charming and courtly Fitzroy. He was a veteran of the Crimean War. Today it is now the home of his grandson, Sir Charles MacLean, Lord-Lieutenant of Argyll, and Chief Scout of the British Commonwealth.

As a lad, Fitzroy was taken to see the ruined castle by his father over a century ago ; and he determined then he would rebuild it one day. It took him sixty years to accomplish his ambition ; and he was 77 years old when he came back and took possession. MacLeans came from all over the world at his invitation to see him enter his newly-built castle. He died in 1937 at the ripe old age of 101 ; and the castle will be standing for another hundred years—and more.

As I have said, the present Sir Charles MacLean is Chief Scout, following in the immortal footsteps of Lord Baden-Powell. He has been Chief Scout since September 1959 ; and he tends a flock of over two million boys of all colours and races throughout the world. Sir Charles, fair-haired, of medium height, is 46 years of age, and is the 27th chief of the clan. In connection with the Scout movement he has been in practically every possible country, and in August 1963 attended the World Jamboree at the ancient battlefield of MARATHON in Greece. His wife, Elizabeth, seldom travels with him abroad : she generally stays at home, holding the fort ; and living in a castle, there is quite a lot of fort !

Continuing round the coast, we come to Grass Point, mentioned earlier (the place of departure for the cattle brought across the island from Croig), and then back to the main road again we come to Loch Spelve, and after a mile or so we come to a junction : the right hand road goes through wild Glen More and eventually to Iona, the left takes us down to Loch Buie.

The Loch Buie road passes through pleasant and varied scenery. There is a renowned Wishing Well on the right of the road shortly after passing Ardura and about one mile from the road junction just named. Carrying on, we come to a lovely inland loch—Loch Uisg—and by the roadside there is a column commemorating Queen Victoria's Jubilee of 1900, set up by the then MacLaine of Loch Buie and his clansmen. Ben Buie (2354 feet high) can be seen rising up on the right. Loch Buie itself is a large sea loch with a fine sandy beach, at Laggan Sands. Further on a track leads to the ancient burial ground of the MacLaines of Loch Buie. (It will be noticed the MacLeans of Duart spell their name differently from these MacLaines of Loch Buie, although both branches claim chieftainship of the clan ; and they are descended from two brothers, and each brother it is said married a daughter of the Lord of the Isles.) At Lochbuie there is a complete Druidical Circle.

At the head of Loch Buie lie the ruins of Moy Castle, ancient stronghold of the MacLaines. 'And now,' said Fiona, as we got out of the car and looked at this ancient monument of stone, 'here is another legend for you ; a true one!' It is known as Ewen of the Little Head.

Ewen was the son of the old chief of Loch Buie, and lived with his henpecking wife in a castle on an island in the middle of a loch bordering on wild Glen More. His wife egged him on to ask his father for more and more land ; and in one argument he struck his father ; and this meant war. Ewen hastened back to his wife and castle, raised men around him, and waited. To take his mind off 'coming events', he went out on the hill after a stag, but as mist was falling fast, he went back to his castle. On the way he saw a fairy woman washing by the burnside ; and putting his troubles to her he asked if she could tell what was going to happen to him in the forthcoming encounter. 'I cannot see so far in this mist,' she said, 'but I believe the battle will be tomorrow; and if your wife gives you butter for breakfast without your asking for it, you will win.'

Next morning, his henpecking, evil wife was in a worse mood than ever ; and poor Ewen got little or no breakfast ; let alone any butter. The battle was joined in Glen More, near the head of Glen Forsa, just near his home loch ; and one stroke of a claymore carried Ewen's head clean off his shoulders. His terrified horse bolted, and, still carrying the headless corpse, eventually reached Moy Castle and pulled up before his father's door.

This story, said Fiona, is close on five centuries old.

No longer is there a MacLaine at Loch Buie and the chief of Loch Buie died in 1909. It is said that Ewen still rides down from the Glen to Castle Moy when there is trouble brewing ; and that sometimes the noise of a ghostly steed is heard, even today, urged on by a ghostly rider. Many down in those parts have heard the horse pass ; but no one has seen any hoof marks in the morning!

I asked Fiona if she believed all this. 'No,' she said, 'not really, but it might have happened, eh ?' 'Aye, and maybe "och aye",' I said. Returning home, we told Mother of the 'ghost riders in the sky' ; but a good hot supper of tripe and onions, scones and cake and everything else that goes with a 'high' tea, soon put this 'high' story out of our heads. 'All tripe,' I said, and we all laughed at this savoury metaphor! 'I wonder what happened to the dear darling of a henpecking wife ?' I said. 'One way of getting rid of your husband, isn't it ?' said Fiona! 'Yes, but that was five hundred years ago, m'dear!' I retorted ; and we all laughed ourselves out of the dim past into the present ; and raising a cup of tea, I said, 'Here's to the future, and no ghostly riders rolling up to our front doors in Mull, or Gairloch!'

Table cleared and dishes washed, as we later sat round having the last cup of tea of the evening, Fiona suddenly said, 'And, oh! yes, there's another nice story situated near where we've been today, at Carsaig Bay and Carsaig Arches, looking across from Loch Buie to the Ross of Mull.' 'Tell us, without any more ado,' we all said, for apparently Mother did not know this yarn either!

'Once upon a time,' said Fiona—'oh! come now', we all echoed, 'this *must* be a fairy tale!'—'there was the old stamping ground of the Cailleach Bhair, the Hag of the Mountains, who used to wade every morning across the Sound of Mull (which took her only knee deep, for she was a giantess) to graze her Highland cow on top of Cruachan (inland from Oban and near Taynuilt).

She had a well up on the crest of Ben Cruachan, a few drops of which she carelessly allowed to overflow one day—hence Loch Awe. Near her grounds, as I have said, are the Carsaig Arches, sixty feet high and carved out by the sea ; and close-by Gorrie's Peak. Now Gorrie was a servant of the chief of Loch Buie, and one day at hunting he was told to guard a pass and head off any deer which might be driven that way. The deer stampeded, but Gorrie could not stop them, try as best he could. His chief, having a cruel temper, punished Gorrie by having him bound and disfigured ; then let him loose.

'The first thing Gorrie did was to seize the chief's only son, who was with his nurse at the time, and run with him in his arms to the edge of the cliff. The chief promised him anything if he would not drop the child over the cliff. In the end Gorrie agreed that if Loch Buie submitted to the same punishment as he had undergone, he would hand back the child. Loch Buie submitted. But Gorrie did not hand back the infant son ; he just looked Loch Buie in the face, smiled . . . and jumped!

The next day when I called as per usual for 'elevenses' coffee, I said to Fiona, 'Well, dear, I think we've now "done" all of Mull, except a visit to Iona ; and as four-fifths of your name spells Iona, what about going over one day and spending a little time there ?' 'Yes, that would be fine'—Fiona's stock comment —'and when shall we go ?'

We arranged the next good day ; and so we set out for Iona— the historic isle ; the cradle of Scottish Christianity—the charm of which, as I said in the previous chapter, lies in the life and work of one single man ; a man with great spiritual faith, and of striking stature—Saint Columba.

CHAPTER 13

IONA

To get to Iona from Tobermory, one needs follow the road south, as we did, to Loch Buie ; but at the head of Loch Spelve, south of Duart Castle, and just before reaching Ardura, one veers right and on through the wilds of Glen More, until the road opens out at the end of the glen for Loch Scridain. Thence one takes the road to the left down through the Ross of Mull (An Ros Muileach) ; *ros* meaning a promontory in the Irish and Gaelic. As we approached here, Fiona had yet another story to tell me, namely, that Loch Scridain owes its existence to the Devil ; for whilst he was having a religious harangue with St. Columba on the top of Ben More, the saint gave him a push. As he sped down the mountainside, finally landing at the bottom, his fall caused a giant cleft, so much so that the sea came bounding in ; and therefore . . . Loch Scridain! To all this, one can imagine our American friends saying, 'Fancy that ; what d'ye know !'

Carrying on, we passed Pennyghael, then Bunessan, and finally Fionphort (where there used to be famous red granite quarries, now lying dormant, but which are still capable of being exploited) where we come to the Iona ferry. Near by Bunessan is Loch Assapol, where in the old days of legend-loving folk, it was said a water-horse lived in the depths of that loch. One day it came ashore and grasped a buxom maiden in front of the minister's eyes and of all the congregation assembled at worship, and carried her into his watery depths. 'There's love again for you,' I said.

As a great deal has been written of Iona (the Sacred Isle)—a tiny island of rock and heather, barely three miles long and about half a mile off the south-west tip of Mull—I purpose giving readers but a very concise account.

To Iona stepped St. Columba—the great apostle of the Northern Picts—from his Irish coracle, sailing from Derry with twelve followers, full of missionary zeal, bringing Christianity to Scotland, on 12th May A.D. 563. He was then 42 years of age.

Fourteen hundred years ago, these thirteen weary men sighted land after a long and hazardous journey across the Irish Sea. Pulling their frail coracle (or curragh) ashore, they would no doubt have knelt down giving thanks to Almighty God for their safe arrival at Iona.

There still stands the little historic, red granite Cathedral or Abbey ; there is still the Street of the Dead, where Scottish kings were carried to their graves. King Brude was the first Pictish king to be buried there (*circa* A.D. 700). Iona, with the graves of upwards of sixty Scottish, Irish and Norwegian kings ; as well as a king of France ; with Celtic crosses that one cannot but view with reverence. Iona, where for nigh on fifteen hundred years, folk have pilgrimaged to this little island where that venerable saint lit a lamp of light which not only illuminated Scotland, but became a power-house radiating its impulses to the ends of the earth ; and the ends of the earth came to visit it also. Sages came for wisdom ; kings for advice, consecration and confession.

Iona, the El Dorado . . .

The present Cathedral dates from the early 13th century, the original abbey being rebuilt by Reginald, Lord of the Isles. It is small and simple, as befits its setting. In 1900 the abbey was gifted to the Church of Scotland by the 8th Duke of Argyll.

Fourteen hundred years ago, St. Columba went up the little mound overlooking the monastery and gave the following blessing :

> Unto this place, small and mean though it be, great homage shall be paid, not only by the kings and peoples of the Scots, but by the rulers of barbarous and distant nations with their peoples. Thy saints also of other churches, shall regard it with no common reverence. . . .

And his last words, before he died on 9th June A.D. 597, aged 76 years, to his brethren around him, were : 'that you preserve with each other, sincere charity and peace'.

In 1938 the Trustees of the abbey gave permission to the 'Iona

H

Community'—a brotherhood of ministers and men, founded by the Rev. Dr. George MacLeod of Govan, a cousin of Dame Flora, Dunvegan Castle, Skye—to restore these ancient buildings; and in 1950 this community was acknowledged by the Church of Scotland, being now part of that denomination.

In the Sound of Iona, opposite the abbey ruins and close to Mull, is the island Eilean nam Ban (Isle of Women), where the wives of the lay-workers lived with the cattle. St. Columba believed in keeping the sex at a distance, for he said, 'Where there is a cow, there will be a woman; and where there is a woman, there will be mischief.'

There is no wildness of scenery in Iona; merely a quiet physical and spiritual beauty; the ruins pointing to peace and humility.

The island is low-lying, with the highest point Dùn-i (*Doon-ee*) in the northern part only 300 feet high. Although the island is treeless, there are many wild flowers and cliff-birds.

Whilst Iona is an island of peace and reverence, it was not always so. From A.D. 797 to A.D. 986, Norsemen raiders came along burning the monastery and killing the monks on the sands of what is still called Martyr's Bay. Monasteries, being rich and defenceless, were special objects of their attack.

Shortly after the Reformation, the monks and nuns were sent into exile, and many valuable manuscripts and books were lost. In the year 1574 the island was given over to the MacLeans of Duart, Mull; and in 1693 it changed hands into the Campbells, with whom it still remains today; their chief being the Duke of Argyll.

During St. Columba's time, Iona was a centre of Celtic art. The Celtic cross is quite distinct from any other form of cross. It combines a ring and a cross—the former intersecting the arms of the latter.

Iona has a population of about 100; and agriculture is the main occupation. There is also the spinning-loom in evidence.

Iona, some three miles by two, is beautiful; it is unique; its atmosphere cannot be equalled anywhere else in the world. It must be seen. Here the last sun-worshippers bowed before their God. One may hear the tide of eternity breaking on the island's shores; an island that fourteen hundred years ago was a bastion of Faith. Many notables and dignitaries of one kind and another lie buried, as might be expected, on ground which was the ancient equivalent of our Westminster Abbey.

Whilst the procession of the dead has long ceased, the pilgrimage goes on . . . and by every denomination of the Christian Church.

To the north of Iona are the Treshnish isles—including the quaint-shaped Dutchman's Cap—and Staffa (eight miles away) with its renowned Fingal's Cave : a 'cathedral' of a very different nature, where the sea rolls out a constant peal of carillons, as it has done since this earth was made. Staffa, an islet formed by volcanic action, is uninhabited. Staffa is violent : Iona, peaceful.

When one goes around the ruins and chapels, looking upon the cluster of Celtic crosses, one feels hushed in the past ; and one talks in whispers . . . as one did in Egypt.

St. Columba, born at Gartan in Co. Donegal in A.D. 521, died in A.D. 597 (twenty-six years after the birth of that great Arab prophet, Mohammed, at Mecca ; founder of the Muslim religion).

Various suggestions were made in 1963 (the fourteenth centenary year of Columba's coming to Iona) of ways in which this nation-making event might be celebrated, bringing true the old Gaelic saying, 'In this Isle of Dreams, God shall yet fulfil Himself anew'. There can be little better than that we should return to an acceptance of the authority of Holy Scripture, as Columba did, taking him as our pattern in the speeding on of the messages throughout the length and breadth of this land, to which he gave so many strenuous years of his life. Death and resurrection are surely evident in these days of pilgrimage to Iona ; with love and peace showing themselves all important.

As a footnote to Iona, one should not forget to record that some 150 years earlier than St. Columba—about A.D. 396— St. Ninian also brought over Christianity to Scotland to the Isle of Whithorn, in Galloway. At the top of the Isle, there still stands the ruins of St. Ninian's Chapel. This so-called isle is now linked by causeway to the mainland, about four miles south of the small burgh of Whithorn (pop. 1000) in Wigtonshire. Whilst St. Ninian did not come over from Ireland, he is supposed to have been born in Galloway, and trained in Italy and France. The stone church he built was known as CANDIDA CASA (the

White House) because it differed from the wooden houses of that period. Ninian and his monks wore woollen undyed cassocks with peaked hoods. Up to the early 15th century, Kings and Queens and ordinary folk came in their pilgrimage there.

Another personality of note who had his roots deep in the thin soil of Mull and Iona was Dr. John MacCormick, one of Scotland's most fervent advocates of 'Home Rule', who died in Glasgow in October 1961, aged but 56 years. He was a lawyer by profession and one of the greatest orators Scotland has produced this century. On his father's side he claimed descent from Cormick, an Irish princeling who followed St. Columba.

In September 1927 he and two friends gave expression to their innermost feelings by founding the Glasgow University Scottish Nationalist Association in a Sauchiehall Street café, which subsequently became the Scottish National party, to secure self-government for Scotland.

But gradually the dream faded and the flood of Nationalism subsided as the various 'lieutenants' melted away.

He was a brilliant man and none will deny he has his place in history with the great patriots of Scotland. He was nicknamed 'King John'.

In short, he was a Wallace of the Word.

Truly in Mull and Iona, there is much to be seen.

There are a number of standing stones scattered throughout Mull; for in pre-Christian days the religion of the Celtic race was Druidism. The rock formation in the Uisken area of the Ross of Mull contains a goodly percentage of elements used in the manufacture of steel.

The Isle of Mull offers great possibilities, too, for coloured photography. 'The Isle of Mull, of isles the fairest.'

CHAPTER 14

CROFT LIFE

THE West Highlands and the Isles have produced a folk-music of singular beauty, songs by the hundred which have the sea and the wind of the Atlantic in them.

One of the loveliest Gaelic songs attributable to Mull is *An t-Eilean Muileach*—'The Isle of Mull' ; a sad and haunting song. The lyric was composed by Dugald Macphail, and there is a large monument raised to him near Ardura, the junction where the road branches off from Glen More to Loch Buie. Macphail wrote the song whilst in exile. I quote what one may call the repeating verse, which I have said is sung to a charming, yet haunting air full of tender emotion :

> The Isle of Mull is of isles the fairest,
> Of ocean gems 'tis the first and rarest ;
> Green-grassy island of sparkling fountains,
> Of waving woods and high-towering mountains.

Mull seems to be more music-minded than up in Wester Ross ; and more dancing and parties arranged. Fiona said she would like to go to Oban during the week of the Mod and hear really good Gaelic music, and this we arranged to do ; and it is the subject of another chapter.

Some of the people in Mull are crofters, but it seemed to us there was nothing like the crofts in Mull as one sees in Wester Ross.

Some of the men still engage in lobster fishing ; and on the hills of Mull are to be seen the golden eagle and red deer (there is a large red deer population protected under the Deer (Scotland) Act of 1959) ; black game seems to have disappeared. The golden eagle, too, appears to be leaving the Scottish Highlands, making for the English Lake District, although eagles have not nested there for over one hundred and fifty years. It seems to be the young, immature eagle that is travelling south—drifters with a wanderlust maybe. But the buzzard apparently abounds. Neither of us had seen so many in our lives before, as that day we went through to Loch Buie. Buzzards on the telegraph poles ; on the 'passing place' standards ; on fences ; everywhere—just sitting and looking. Sometimes as we passed and the noise of the car disturbed their dreams, they would circle overhead with superb grace, their plaintive mews mingling with the notes of the curlews, all of which echoed back to us from the hills close by.

We also passed, on that run, a few seals basking on some of the rocks in Loch Spelve ; when I blew the horn, they darted under water, only to come up out again a minute later. Very inquisitive animals, seals! Owing to the alleged increase in recent years of the grey seal population, the Secretary of State for Scotland decided to relax protection, during the 1960 breeding season, hitherto afforded by the 1932 Protection Act. The Nature Conservancy is undertaking a special three-year scientific study of grey seals, which are believed to be damaging coastal salmon fisheries in Scotland ; and has recommended suspension of the Close Season for the next five years, as little is known of their habits.

CROFTING. The definition of a croft is given by a frustrated crofter as 'a small piece of land surrounded by regulations'. The story is told of an old crofter in Mull, who, whilst talking with a visitor, complained of the increasing amount of smoke on the island. 'Smoke ?' the visitor asked, looking dumbfounded, for all around him was green grass, heather, valleys and hills. 'Yes,' the crofter said, 'too much smoke from the cars of all the government officials that keep coming and going !'

A croft is a little field adjoining a wee dwelling-house ; agricultural smallholdings in fact ; a land-holding of not more than seventy-five acres for the largest. There are seven crofting counties in Scotland—Argyll, Inverness, Ross and Cromarty, Sutherland, Caithness, Orkney and Zetland ; and it can be appreciated this includes a wide variety of ground from the rich land in the east to the peat and bare rocks of the west. There are about 20,000 crofts, of which only 2000 are of more than fifty acres. In the islands and the West Highlands, the majority are about three or four acres only. The land worked may be a small patch among rocks, the soil being scraped into ridges and potatoes planted ; or fields reclaimed from the heather and bracken. In

the summer most crofters let their cottage to visitors, whilst the
crofter and his family live in a makeshift shed at the back. Life
doing that is hard with all the croft work to attend to as well ;
crofting and tourism may not go well together ? On the land
there has been for generations a crippling lack of capital to effect
improvements or buy machinery. It is said crofters are making
as good use of their land as the men on the bigger upland farms.
But they cannot make a living on present-day standards from
crofting alone, and the economists say the reason is the majority
of crofts are too small, and their resources far too limited to give
an adequate volume of output. Money is still required to be
spent constructively, and legislation to accompany same. Hitherto,
the central government has generally given but a niggardly
amount of money to carry out a 'rebirth' of the land economy of
the Highlands.

A Crofters Commission was set up years ago to help them
out of their difficulties. A year or so past this Commission set
about seeking powers to 'rationalise crofting agriculture', which
of course obviously meant dispossessing crofters, who by reason
of absence, disability or age, were not working their land to
advantage ; throwing crofts together and so forth. Throughout
the years, the crofting system has survived all these rigours and
pitfalls to a remarkable degree. In social terms it is very effective :
it gives inner joy and satisfaction to the people in their gaining
happiness from the produce of their soil.

A new Crofters Act came into force on 27th August 1961 in
which provisions are made for sub-letting, but which will not
affect their tenure in any way. The main change provided in this
new Act is to get more crofting land under cultivation by reorganising the township and sub-letting crofts to create bigger
holdings; but no such reorganising of any township would be
attempted without the majority consent of the members.

Much has been blamed on the crofters themselves, such as
lacking in initiative and unwilling to help themselves ; but such
accusations more often than not come from people without intimate understanding of crofting conditions, or of human beings
who for generations have experienced depression and poverty
and who through such lengthy endurances are not able to sur-
mount difficulties unaided ; and many lose heart.

Nothing is really possible without money. In the past the

Highlands must have been the most expensive area in Britain from the point of view of money given in Public Assistance, poor relief and unemployment benefits. Unproductive money is money down the drain, and the Highlands have been dubbed 'an area of a receiving character ; a subsidised land'.

However, from my experience and knowledge they serve the country well ; and they are not ashamed of their heritage. I have yet to meet a crofter who is not a most likeable person and character. A number of them may be poorly off, living in wee cottages through whose doors luxury has never entered. But they still live in *Tìr nan Òg*—the land of the ever-young.

They are a worthy, if not a wealthy, folk.

The Gaelic communities in the islands and of Wester Ross, are one of the oldest remaining cultures in Europe, possessing the same roots as the Irish Gaels, with whom they used to consider themselves to be one people. Then there is the oral tradition— the folk tales and historical legends from ancient days still on the lips of those in the islands and the north-west.

The Highlander will put forward his whole effort if a reasonable profit is at the end of his labours. If there are no proper roads, no transport, no steamers calling to create life and prosperity—well, he can't build or make them himself ; so logically, in the far-away spots, he says, 'I'll let the world go by'. After all—Will the peats dig themselves ? Will the fish jump ashore ?

To his eternal credit, the Highlander has all the virtues of a generous man—a sense of humour, a sense of companionship, a sense of occasion. There are still people of genius and drive in Scotland today ; people who can—if they will—achieve distinction. The whole character of the nation is tough and resilient ; Scottish labour is acknowledged as second to none ; its natural resources in the Highlands, rivers, glens and scenery are hard to outstrip.

It makes gloomy reading those terrible days when a people were forced by poverty and sometimes by other men's greed to cross the seas to a new home—the 'clearances' after the '45 Jacobite rebellion in which hundreds of thousands of clansmen were banished ; the forfeiture of clan estates, and the disintegration of that social system ; glens emptied—even the aged and sick being mercilessly ejected, their cottages and furniture burned. 'Prince Charlie's Year' to be sure!

Years of famine came, unrelieved by any government assistance, when people scratched along the beaches for food; being liable to be evicted at their factor's whim. It was not until the Crofters Act of 1886, following the Napier Commission's report of 1883, that security of tenure and fair rents came to be established—exactly one hundred and forty years after 'Charlie's Year'.

One may ask why the Highlanders did not offer more resistance to the inhumanity of those clearances? One factor was their God-fearing nature; many of their ministers told them it was the Will of God. And another cause was the young active males were away in the Napoleonic wars, fighting for the very people and government that was clearing them away; and when they returned they found their homes and people gone.

Great strains; great hardships; all making for sad reading. But this, in its stark reality, is the background to crofting; a history founded on mistrust on an exhausted population.

Since the 'clearances', crofting in the Highlands has never been the same. To put it bluntly, to my mind, it 'knocked the stuffing' out of this Highland industry; and then again, the Highlands are so far away from the markets.

The Crofters Commission, born of good intentions, appears to me, however, to have lost a certain impetus, and seems to be just another branch of St. Andrew's House. There are several bodies and organisations of one sort or another interested in land in Scotland. It would be better for more unification of interests. No government or body can expect to stem several hundred years of deterioration, putting it on a solid foundation in a matter of a year or so; and a comprehensive land commission—freed from all political pressure—would be the ideal set-up. The integration of forestry and agriculture, as would seem to be the trend, would take another hundred years to fructify. For years the Highlander has been the self-imposed concern of industrial magnates turned lairds. Whilst the lairds have largely disappeared, they have left the Highlander as 'naebody's bairn'. Transport charges are extortionate in the Highlands, and thereby strangle a lot of trade and folk where ancillary employment is not at hand. It has been proved that small local light industries are economic; the labour is there, the choice of siting unlimited. So what?

The tourism harvest is but seasonal : I am sure visitors can see and appreciate the crofters' problems in making a living. As I have just said, they are indeed a worthy folk. Authority must act, and move. The Highlands should not be allowed to go forwards, backwards. I have seen it reported that many absurd questions are asked of crofters, such as 'What is your yield of silage per acre?'—where silage is not grown. 'What are your suggestions for the manure needed?'—in a rainfall where any application of consequence would be washed out in a matter of months.

Today the position brightens somewhat; a grow-more-flower-bulbs drive started in the spring of 1961 throughout the Western Isles. Scotland's 'little Holland' has plots of bulbs in Lewis, Harris, Barra, North and South Uist, Tiree, Coll, Mull and Islay. The growers—mostly crofters—have their own concern, The Hebridean Bulb Growers Ltd.; a large number of bulbs are graded and packed in Tiree. In my Gairloch domain I have dozens of such daffodil bulbs from Tiree; and they do wonderfully well, their finely-shaped trumpets blowing fanfares heralding spring. It is thought Oban, as a centre, would suit the majority of growers. Undoubtedly there is a big future for Hebridean bulbs, and it could well be great help to the Western Isles, if the crofters developed this line of business in all earnestness, for it is reckoned a net profit of around £300 an acre could be expected from bulb growing; and an acre is not much for a crofter to handle along with the running of his own croft. The sale is for bulbs—not flowers.

There is a phenomenal re-seeding of moorland on the island of Lewis. In Shetland there is a lobster-marketing board; and the crofter-fishermen from around there have increased the value of such fish handed in to the storage tanks at Scalloway by nearly 800 per cent in seven years. There is, too, a thriving marketing arrangement for eggs in South Uist.

A crofter in Bunessan, Mull, has recently succeeded in growing grass which it is thought may revolutionise livestock-rearing in the Highlands. The grass is a kind of tussock, found almost exclusively in the Falkland Islands; the grass keeps green all the year round. In the Falklands, even poor cattle put on this grass come into fine fettle within two months; and sheep achieve top condition in just over three weeks.

In so far as Mull is concerned, that island was also depleted during the clearances to an alarming degree. Taking but one instance, the small isle of Ulva, which I have mentioned, off the western coast of Mull, once had a population of 700. In the last Census (1961) there were only 30 people on both Ulva and Gometra, its near-by isle. In fact in Mull—considering its size and pasture land—we saw very few crofts ; quite a few 'sporting estates' and big houses, but, as I have said, few crofts. We were told the island had been a patchwork of such estates from the 'evictions' up till now. The sporting estate can easily be distinguished—a mansion-house type of building, a salmon river and a panoramic view of desolate hills ; and humans kept down to a minimum. And those owners are in residence for only a few weeks in the summer. There are today in Mull over one dozen tenant farms, and only a hundred, or even less, small, odd crofts. For its size, there is more nobility in Mull than in any other part of Britain.

The estate around Treshnish belongs to Lady Rankine, lady-in-waiting to the Queen Mother ; Lady Congleton owns the island of Ulva ; Major Howarth, the adjoining isle of Gometra. A Major Compton owns the territory Treshnish to Laggan, bordering Loch Tuath ; Campbell K. Finlay, the writer, lives near Dervaig.

I mentioned the name of David Livingstone in the first chapter of this book. Although David was born in Blantyre, Lanarkshire, his father was of Highland stock, and from Mull ; for his grandfather, known as Neil Mhor, married Mary Morison, a native of Mull, settling on the island for some time, and thence over to a croft on the isle of Ulva, where Neil Beag (David's father) was born. In 1792 Neil Mhor went south with his family of three sons and four daughters to Blantyre, where Neil Beag married Agnes Hunter ; and there, David Livingstone, the famous, was born.

A Council of Social Service has recently been formed in Mull, and it is hoped to persuade the government to adopt a plan for the rehabilitation of the island ; and a development scheme is envisaged for communications, social services, agriculture, small industries and weaving.

Mull is larger than some of the Scottish counties ; and since the war, owners discovered that castles are not only out of date, but far too expensive to keep up. It was found that the Forestry Commission was willing to buy any parcel of land on an estate, and that they would undertake to do a great deal of fencing thereon if the land was conveniently sold in selected portions; and thus a large amount of selling took place, during which time the Commission bought over 50,000 acres in Mull.

Comparisons of acreage and population in the inner and outer isles produce startling interest and food for thought, for the need of land being available to the people of Mull.

	Acreage	*Population*
Lewis and Harris	528,000	33,600
Skye and Raasay	420,000	11,000
South Uist	90,000	4,900
North Uist	75,500	3,300
Mull	225,000	2,000

Surely this 'land case' for Mull is one for serious—very serious—consideration by the Scottish Office?

Mull, being so sparsely populated, and with a winding coast line of over 300 miles, is therefore an ideal island for tourists to visit, who look for peace and quiet, and to be away from the hurly-burly of town routine. In this respect it is even better than Skye, which has a population over five times that of Mull.

Of course, in some crofting districts there are to be seen many patches of reeds and spiky thistles on the land, and if the Commission has its eyes on same, it should also examine the reasons for them. The two wars would be the answer, for the menfolk had no reserved protection on returning. A man may not work his croft fully now, because whilst he went off fit to fight for his land, he maybe came back disabled.

However, let us hope that, with the new Crofters Act, together with suggestions I have made, the crofter will get a promise of security, as well as a proper and fair deal for the future. And to all crofters, I add my salute of *Slàinte Mhath !*

'What do you think of the Common Market?' a visitor once asked a crofter. 'Och, it would be all right,' he said, 'so long as they hold it on a Friday!'

I would remind readers that the islands, and also where I live in Wester Ross, are not a land of luxury living by any means. But who wants that, if there are so many other compensating factors, which you simply cannot get elsewhere? Luxury? It is too often a let-down; for the more you acquire, the more acquisitive you get.

There is an old Chinese saying, 'Possessions are like a drug ; he more you have, the more you want'.

A washing-machine may be a woman's heart's desire. If only you had that, you'd be perfectly happy. You get it. And hen ? The machine is heaven but you still have to hang out the clothes on a biting cold day or festoon them around the kitchen grate when it rains. So you begin to have, deep down, an aching desire for a spin-drier to make life perfect. This you get from your fond husband's pay-packet ; then a dish-washer, and a potato peeling machine, for your hands get so rough and red peeling potatoes and washing-up day in and day out!

There is no luxury in the world that can be said to be the last ; each new gadget breeds another new gadget ; and no money can buy enduring contentment and happiness. That comes only from within ; and that 'within' can be abundantly satisfied by the glory of nature seen in Mull, and the west coast in its ever-changing moods over the seas and bays and to the mountains in the distance—and with the people who inhabit these parts of Scotland.

Since the war hydro-electric schemes have proved a godsend to the crofters and to the Highlanders in general. They have provided work for thousands in the straths and glens, together with goodly wage packets. In fact, it is true to say, they have 'dammed' Highland depopulation by stopping the drift south of many skilled and unskilled men.

Since 1946 the North of Scotland Hydro-Electric Board has spent £200 million on development. And one of the most pleasing features of their schemes has been that they have been carried out in an unbroken sequence. When the Glen Affric project was finished, there was the Orrin one just across the Ross-shire hills ; the Shin scheme in Sutherland ; and then there was the £14 million Kilmorack-Strathfarrar undertaking employing some 1400 men. When one scheme was completed, the Highland workers merely 'shifted camp'. There is the Glen Nevis scheme ; and so this chain of events could be continued for another ten years, thereby preventing another Highland 'clearance' for some time to come.

Again, early in 1963, after centuries of neglect, diminishing hopes and dwindling population in the Highlands, have come many light industries, particularly the dramatic agreement by the government of the day to the establishment of a £20 million pulp mill at Fort William, which mighty project will transform and uplift the very life of the Highlander ; indeed it will rejuvenate and revolutionise life throughout the Western Highlands as never before, for its impact will be felt for hundreds of miles around. New life-blood will rush back from the cities to the Highlands, and Hector and Roddie will return to the love and labour in their native surroundings and under their own majestic hills which they had no alternative but to leave years ago. In fact, a resurgence of the traditional Highland way of life.

Many a rainbow will curve over the bog and heather of their early days. This Mill—this new venture—will take in trees at one end, turning out paper at the other : 80,000 tons of it yearly by the end of 1965.

So to all these various schemes, bringing hope and prosperity to the Highlands, we can proudly say *Slàinte Mhath !*

CHAPTER 15

THE MOD

THE Mod is a yearly festival of Gaelic music, song, dance, oral competition and the like ; and it is held for a week at different centres each year and to which all Gaelic-lovers (gentle Gaels with true speech on their lips) wend their way, young—even the very young—and old ; for music is a universal language ; a language which all the world understands, be it Gaelic or otherwise.

At one time, before I became acquainted with Scotland, I used to imagine MOD was something you ate, or the name of a Cornish wine!

The vocabulary of Gaelic is much greater, and less defiled, than most ; it is not a 'mongrel' language like English. Gaelic is a clear-cut, pedigreed language, with a subtle gradation of meaning in the words it employs. It is a living, and therefore a spoken language, though it is sorrowful to think fewer and fewer people speak it nowadays, despite early schooling aid and efforts.

The Gael's contribution is a valuable one ; his language, song, poetry and story enhance the arts of the world. And it has been said by distinguished Gaelic scholars 'if Gaelic dies, then it is a loss to civilisation'. It may be giving ground, but it is still as full of life up in the real Highland territory as a flowering hawthorn tree—and at the Mods, well, Gaeldom runs riot!

The longing for things gone beyond recall is probably the most moving note in Gaelic poetry ; not so much Celtic gloom, but rather the hard facts of a people forced by poverty and by other men's greed years ago, to cross the seas to new homes, as I have stated already. Gaelic is more a language of description.

Fiona had said she would love to attend a Mod, and as it was shortly to be staged in Oban (the very first Mod—*vide* Chapter 10 —was held in that town in 1892), we arranged our plans to go over there for two or three days, leaving bakery and foodstuffs in ample supply for Mother and Colin whilst we were away.

We left by the morning steamer—leaving the car on the pier for the few days we were to be 'overseas'—reaching Oban by noon : booked in at the hotel and after lunch set about surveying the town's decorations put up for this auspicious event.

As I have remarked, every year these great Mods are held, Gaeldom abandons itself to a week of glorious music and the renewing of auld acquaintances. There is the thrill of the tartans, the joy of meeting old friends and 'feeling' the soft touch of the Gaelic accent, their lingering on the 'r's'; the softened consonants. The Mod is a unique gathering; colourful, impressive and electrifying. As someone once said, 'A gran' language the Gaelic; profanity in it just sounds like poetry in any other tongue!'

The word 'mod' comes from a word 'mot', so Gaelic scholars say, which is common to Norse and to Anglo-Saxon, but whether it came to us from the Vikings is uncertain.

The Mod is not an entirely musical festival such as some would suppose; for at the last Mod held, over 40 per cent of the entries in the junior section were for the oral competitions, which is indicative of the desire of Highland youth to become proficient in the Gaelic language.

Invariably on the Sunday before 'the week' commences there is a traditional Gaelic service held in the town's main church, which is attended by the Provost, Magistrates and members of the Town Council.

We toured the town, hand in hand, keyed up with 'mod-itis', for which they say the only cure is whisky, or other spirits—to bring back the 'spirits' of the past, I suppose! Fiona wore a tartan skirt and a check-tartan coat, for it was none too warm a day; and she looked real bonnie. I had on my 'fore-and-aft' deer-stalker hat, trying to look the part of a Highland laird from Mull—not that it suits me, but one needed to dress according to the 'atmospherics'. An English lady stopped us, saying, 'Please can you tell me where this Mod is?' That was a good question! It was all over the town!

Oban was full to bursting point; about 10,000 more people, they told us, had added themselves on to the resident population; and all saying it was to be the most memorable days of a most memorable Mod—with a certain amount of 'slurring' of that phrase!

Cars and lorries drove in and out with carefree abandon.

Everyone of any note or having any Highland connections at all seemed to be milling around. All had swept into this peaceful town on this week of 'Operation Mod'.

Those behind the cocktail bars were working and sweating at high pressure—breakneck speed—right through the day and the night unto the dawn ; probably trying to put thirty hours into the twenty-four. Cash registers would need a general overhaul after the mad Mod days ; for the bells would probably be worn out, or jammed !

Meals were not the only things that 'staggered' in Mod week ; and no one ever seemed to go to bed. Cattle too were being driven along the High Street. 'Are they to be at the Mod ?' I asked Fiona. Laughingly she said, 'No, darling, it so happens there's a cattle sale this very week of all weeks!'

Some were Highland, shaggy cattle that had 'come to town' ; wide, wide horns, spread six feet or so ; and more so as the night wore on! and they could give you a nasty jerk in the back and drag your coat off should you happen to get in their track. However, the Gaelic tradition is bound up with such beasts, the byre and sheep. So who cared ?

Yes, people who wanted to meet others similarly imbued ; people who wanted to sing and dance in the old traditional way, were there ; for to such folk their songs draw strength from their wild hills and misty moors ; warm and fragrant from the heather ; and amongst the whole assembly of such kindly folk, kith and kin are woven and knitted together like the strands of wool in the Fair Isle jerseys still being made by old knitters in out-of-the-way places.

These songs of the isles delight all ears—even English ears— as do the gaily-coloured kilts (with hues like the tint of heather, the greens resembling moss) swinging and swirling ; that and the women wearing the brooches of their respective clans.

Tartan uppermost and everywhere ; the shops making beautiful displays in their windows ; and the Council had 'gone to town' also in stretching a banner across the main thoroughfare emblazoned with the words CEUD MÌLE FÀILTE (100,000 welcomes) ; a cheering thought even on this cold day. I suspect many English folk would enquire of the first Highlander in a kilt they met on the street, as to what 'those foreign words mean ?'

I

And if the six-foot tall, hairy-kneed kiltie was the usual Highland wag, he would tell them in all seriousness that it literally meant 'I can't give you anything but love!'

Most of the elderly women who steadfastly attend these Mods, and who come from all quarters of the Highlands and Islands, are of a shy, retiring disposition ; but the memories of song and laughter still abound in their bosoms. And as these women and wives (some mayhap bereft of their menfolk) listen to the young performers ('the young in heart'), they smile happily to the speech and to the tradition which, to them, is a sure and living force ; for there are things which can be expressed only in Gaelic ; truths in life that can only be put to Gaelic verse. For life in the Highlands is hard, as hard and as dreary as the barren rocks that surround them and their crofts ; yet, all the same, the love of life lies lightly on their chiselled faces.

Young farmers have left their crofts for the week, and whilst they are away their cattle will be roaming the hillside at leisure, crushing back the old invader—the bracken. Some of the youngsters only have enough money saved to come for the one day they are 'performing' ; and then back they must go to their homes, which may be in one of the far-away islands of the Outer Hebrides. A hard existence ; a 'stocky' people indeed.

Young and old ; junior choirs, assiduously coached by their Gaelic teacher, come to relive, to revitalise one part—and to them *the* part—of Scottish home life which, to these young boys and girls, spells contentment of their own wee Highland homes. Until they grow up—and there's the rub.

It may be recorded with pride that Ross-shire has the highest percentage of Gaelic speakers of all the counties. But the language is dying out. Earnest followers of Gaelic maintain, however, that the language will be spoken a thousand years from now. But people talked like that about the old Norse language which faded out in Shetland hundreds of years ago ; as they did about Cornish, which died out in Cornwall in the mid-1700's.

In 1800 one Scotsman in five spoke Gaelic.

In 1860 the ratio was one in ten.

In 1962 it was about one in seventy.

For some generations now Highlanders have been brought up in the comfortable belief that they can preserve their character, customs and traditions, and yet allow their language to perish.

The decline in the number of Gaelic speakers is due in no small measure undoubtedly to depopulation. Many of the Western Isles carry less than a third of the population they had a hundred years ago ; and the same process is going on all over the Highlands today. In my own Gairloch parish census there were 5000 people in 1880 ; but only 1763 in the year of 1961—a drop of over 60 per cent in eighty years.

Generally speaking, apart from isolated pockets throughout the Highlands, the Gaelic-speaking communities are almost entirely confined to the islands and the districts along the north-west coast.

After three gloriously happy days (though weather not so glorious) we returned home to Mull, to Mother and Colin. It *was* nice to be back and to see them, and to tell them all we had seen and done ; and they themselves were so glad to see us—you would almost have thought we had been away three months instead of three days! But such are the feelings of a dear family ; and dear they were to me, all of them ; the dearest I had ever known in my life.

We felt a little sad—that it was a great pity—to think that Gaelic was dying and decaying. It just seemed to us to be the fading language of the home, of the fishermen and of the croft ; and not the language of the enlarging commercial and industrial world in which we are being so rapidly engulfed.

One cannot revive a language by literary efforts or arguments alone. It can only be revived when its appeal reaches down to the deepest sentiments of a people, or a race ; when their faith and their passions become aroused to the full.

Therefore I would say to all the 'young in heart', 'Forward the Gaelic' ; *Suas Leis à Ghàidhlig !*

And I put the question very pointedly, 'Who will take up the claymore for the Highlands and the Islands ?' I incline to believe the main support must come from inside Scotland itself ; for the only people who can save Gaeldom are the Gaels themselves. And I hope that sinks in.

At the Annual General Meeting of An Comunn Gaidhealach (the Gaelic Association or League) in Stirling in 1961, there was much talk of a 'wind of change' to whistle through the whole structure of the Association, to blow away out-of-date methods and ideas. And it may be that this wind blows from the north to the south, rather than south to north, as has been the case previously. For the Standing Committees of the Executive Council, which deals with the Gaelic Youth (in whose hands, as I have said, lies the future of Gaelic as a living language, together with the whole Gaelic culture and way of life), elected their youngest convener to their council for many years; and the only convener for quite some time who has been domiciled in the north.

That person was Kay Matheson, of the 'Stone of Destiny' adventure, vividly described in *And It Came to Pass*. This, indeed, is a great honour to a comparatively young girl teaching in Gairloch, close beside where I write this book.

It may well be that a fresh, cold northerly wind blowing from Wester Ross will revive the warm, sluggish southerly wind from the Association's Glasgow headquarters! I sincerely hope it does; a 'Gael' force wind, shaking the whole movement into advantage, and into more activity than ever before. *Slàinte Mhath !*

CHAPTER 16

THE SABBATH

As mentioned before, Fiona and family were members of
the Free Church ; and as I came to know them better
and gradually merged into the warmth of their household,
I used to spend most Sundays with them in the restfulness of their
domain, reading many of the religious books they had ; the lives
of great preachers and missionaries. The Free Church Bookroom
and the Banner of Truth Trust produce many practical expositions
of the Gospel texts from many able writers ; and I found much
to improve my knowledge upon both the Old and the New
Testaments, which took me back—as did the Pyramids—the
many thousand years of creation. Often I felt I was touching
Time's infinite realm, realising that all creation was in a state of
renewal ; what is, had existed before, and what is lost will return
again . . . all things beginning when they have passed away ;
that nothing perishes but which may be recovered. And this
revolving order is evidence of resurrection. There is a great deal
to be learned in such readings, and in the constructive ways in
which nature reveals itself. The earth seems to receive instruction
from Heaven to reclothe the bare trees ; to colour the flowers
afresh ; to spread out the grass again and to resurrect the buried
seeds.

In Mull and Wester Ross one cannot fail to notice in nature
the presence of some unseen hand, year in and year out ; verily
beauty is a door to God.

At every meal grace was said—as is the acknowledged custom

in the Highlands—and thanks given for our many blessings ; food had been prepared the night before, potatoes peeled, vegetables ready ; soup and pudding made. All that was required on the Sabbath was just to bring everything to the boil. A day of rest and peace.

I used to take them all to the Kirk at Tobermory, generally to the evening service ; and those Sundays will remain in my memory for all time. We listened to many beautiful sermons ; sermons delivered by the minister straight from the heart for a whole hour, without any notes or references whatsoever.

Fiona's household was wrapt in Faith ; faith, the substance of things hoped for ; the evidence of things not seen. By faith, Abel offered unto God a more excellent sacrifice than Cain. By faith, Noah, moving with fear, prepared an ark to the saving of his house ; by faith, Abraham went out, not knowing whither he went, to a far place which he was to inherit ; he sojourned in the land of promise ; through faith his wife Sarah received strength to conceive when she was long past age ; by faith, Moses refused to be called the son of Pharaoh's daughter, and by faith he led the children of Israel through the Red Sea as by dry land, which the Egyptians assaying to do, were drowned. By faith, the walls of Jericho fell, after being encompassed seven days. And in my own case, by faith I felt I would, in time, be happily rewarded. And Fiona was that reward ; Fiona who, when I met her, was a little more than half the allotted span of three score years and ten ; yet she had inborn youth akin to my own ; and love seemed to make us younger each and every day. It helped us over all our daily chores. We seemed to be 'born again', treading as it were upon a thick-piled carpet, which had an equally thick and re-silient underlay.

Scotland as a whole is a Church-minded nation to a far greater extent than England, so that in such a context the Church of England is relatively the junior partner. Church membership in Scotland is $2\frac{1}{2}$ times what it is in England. It will appear galling to some devout Scots ministers when the Church of England is projected as 'the National Church in Britain'. In fact, only about 10 per cent of the English adult population can lay claim to full Church membership ; whereas the Church in Scotland can claim 66 per cent of the adult population to Church membership.

Rather staggering figures, surely ? It is predominantly Protestant ; and the smaller the religious denominations, the more loyal the members. On a normal Sunday one million adults in Scotland attend at least one service ; sometimes two services.

Yes, Scotland—particularly the Highlands—has deep religious feelings.

The Free Church of Scotland and the Free Presbyterian Church of Scotland strictly adhere to all the Bible says. Under the name of Holy Scripture—or the Word of God, written— are contained all the Books of the Old and New Testaments ; all of which are given by inspiration of God, to be the rule of faith and life. The Books, they maintain, commonly called Apocrypha—not being of divine inspiration—are no part of the canon of the scripture ; and therefore are of no authority in the Church of God.

The Free and the Free Presbyterian Churches have, as their acknowledged text-book, *The Confession of Faith*, dealing exhaustively with every aspect of scriptural life from the Creation to the Last Judgement ; agreed upon by the Assembly of Divines at Westminster as a part of the Covenanted Uniformity in Religion betwixt the Churches of Christ in the Kingdoms of Scotland, England and Ireland, and approved by the General Assembly in 1647, and ratified by Acts of Parliament 1649 and 1690, as the public and avowed Confession of the Church of Scotland. . . .

And these words, which I command thee this day, shall be in thine heart ; and thou shalt teach them diligently unto thy children, and shalt talk of them when thou sittest in thine house, and when thou walkest by the way, and when thou liest down, and when thou risest up.—Deut. vi, 6, 7.

The Old Testament in Hebrew (which was the native language of the people of God of old) and the New Testament in Greek (which at the time of the writing of it was most generally known to the nations) being immediately inspired by God, they hold to be authentic, being by singular care and providence kept pure throughout all the ages.

Although they acknowledge all things in Scripture are not alike plain in themselves, yet in searching through The Book, one will come across, in some place or another, a clear understanding of the word.

Truly, the fourth commandment—remember the Sabbath

day, to keep it holy—is rigorously observed in the Highlands. One whole day in seven was surely appointed in the Scriptures. This was the seventh, or the last day of the week, from the beginning of the world to the resurrection of Christ ; and the first day of the week ever since, which in Scripture is called The Lord's Day ; and so it will continue to the end of the world as the Christian Sabbath.

The lonely, barren, treeless island of Iona, as I have said previously, situated about one mile off the south-west extremity of Mull, is the cradle of Scottish Christianity, for in the year A.D. 563 St. Columba landed here from Ireland with twelve companions (disciples), established a monastery, and used the island as a base for his evangelistic journeys.

One of the most significant events in Scots ecclesiastical history was the *Disruption of 1843*, when what came to be called the Free Church split from the Church of Scotland on the ancient and sorry issue of patronage.   That was an event of a most dramatic order, the ministers so opposed sacrificing their livings with selflessness that must be respected ; and congregations suffering forms of martyrdom—if only mild—for the sake of a conception of religious liberty.   The people rebelled when worthless men were appointed to big parishes by lay patrons, quite regardless of their being suitable or unsuitable.

In Scotland it is held that Church history should take into consideration that the origin of the Church in the world came from God directly, and that He commanded Moses to do all things according to the pattern shown him on the Mount.   This Moses did.   But as time went on, the leaders of the people both in temporal and in spiritual matters departed from the prescribed worship by uniting it with the idolatrous mode of worship observed by the heathens around them.   Every time they had, by their own policy, strayed from the worship originally ordained they were plunged into wars, famines and pestilences, and were brought into untold miseries by one nation after another.   Whilst great men were to come forward to deliver them from their enemies, they could not for long be kept from idolatry, until at long last they were banished to Babylon for seventy years.   Whilst this cured them of idolatry it did not cure them of mixing their own policy with the Word and worship of God, and so at last they were thrust out of their own land.   The history of the Church reveals that, even during the lifetime of the Apostles, heresies began to appear.   The letters to the Seven Churches of Asia, recorded in Revelations, show how far some of those Churches had departed from the faith and purity of worship.

The Free Church of Scotland, at her separation in 1843, claimed that she adhered to the Creed and Constitution of the Established Church of Scotland in their entirety, and that she *had to separate* on account of the intrusion of the civil courts into the spiritual jurisdiction of the Church courts, in order to maintain the lawful rights of the Established Church of Scotland.   In one word, that she was the Church of Scotland, *free* ;   following the Church's original Calvinistic preachings to the letter.

When the Disruption took place in 1843, the party who contended for the spiritual independence of the Church of Scotland— for the non-interference by the civil courts (magistrates) in matters belonging to the spiritual jurisdiction of the courts of the Church —took every precaution to make their position crystal clear.   The Claim, Declaration and Protest of 1842, regarding the encroachment of the Court of Session, leaves no doubt that the Disruption Fathers contended for the rights of the Church of Scotland as established by law.   The two main claims put forward were (1) that 'there is no other head of the Church but the Lord Jesus Christ', and (2) that 'the Lord Jesus, as King and Head of His Church, had appointed a government in the hands of church officers distinct from the civil magistrate, which government is ministerial, not lordly, and to be exercised in consonance with the laws of Christ, and with the liberties of His people'.   In the law of Scotland the spiritual courts of the Church and the secular courts were co-ordinate, not subordinate the one to the other, in their own spheres of action.

The *Free Church* held this view unimpaired when she had in 1843, for truth and conscience' sake, to give up all the churches, manses, glebes and salaries, and all the remuneration which accrued to her from State connection, in order to maintain Christ's right to rule in His own Church by His Word in the hands of her own office - bearers.   Those who fought for these rights recorded explicitly that they were compelled to relinquish State connection on account of the intrusion of the civil courts into the spiritual province of the Church by forcing ministers on congregations contrary to the wishes of the people and in defiance of the Church's courts, and *not* because they ceased to hold the doctrine of the Establishment of Religion by the State to be a Scriptural doctrine and highly valued by them.

This then was the position of the Free Church at the Disruption.

There were certain obstacles existing between the Free Church and the United Presbyterian Church (another body that had welded together certain other 18th-century seceders, anti-burghers and such-like—burghers being the name of a sect of seceders from the Church of Scotland), and at the General Assembly of the Free Church in 1863 a large committee was appointed to see whether these obstacles could be removed so that a Union of the two bodies might come about.

Much bitter feeling arose in discussions, so much so that at the Assembly of 1867 five members of the Free Church committee resigned. There then arose two parties opposing each other known as the *Unionists* and the *anti-Unionists*, and as time went on these divergent positions and views began to unfold themselves. The Free Church party was led by Dr. Begg of Edinburgh and Dr. Nixon of Montrose ; whilst the other party, who were more for adopting a compromising solution, was led by Dr. Rainy and Dr. Candlish.

Strife entered into the very heart of the Free Church. Instead of the Union that was contemplated in 1863, and so much desired, internal discussions and strife originated which at last broke up the Church into fragments.

A large minority deplored the baneful effects of the union controversy on the peace and spiritual prosperity of the Free Church ; of the Free Church being rent into two opposing camps.

It was in *May 1893* at the General Assembly that the Rev. Donald Macfarlane of Raasay, making strong protests over past events, separated from the Free Church and many applauded and followed in his bold step, and upon his preaching to a congregation worshipping at Millhouse, Kames, formed itself into the first congregation of what was to be known afterwards as the *Free Presbyterian Church*.

On his return to Raasay, Mr. Macfarlane received much encouragement and many meetings were subsequently held in different parts of the West of Scotland, when it was decided that immediate steps be taken to form a Presbytery. In July 1893 the

Revs. Macfarlane, D. Macdonald (Shieldaig) and Mr. Alex. Macfarlane (schoolmaster, Raasay) met and formed '*The Free Presbyterian Church Presbytery of Scotland*'.

At a meeting on *14th August 1893* at Portree, the Presbytery
adopted the Deed of Separation. At a further meeting that month
(30th August) a call was moderated to Rev. John R. MacKay ;
and MacKay's ordination and induction took place at Gairloch
in the golf-course hollow—the *Leabaidh na bà Baine*—on 11th
October 1893.

He was the first minister ordained in the Free Presbyterian
Church.

This, then, was the small beginning of the Free Presbyterian
Church taken out of the Free Church. The F.P. Church then
had but two ministers and a few students only.

On *30th October 1900*, the Union Act was passed : *i.e.* the
Free Church duly united with the United Presbyterian Church,
becoming known as the United Free Church of Scotland—or the
present Free Church ; a famous union, and it produced the
notorious litigation which gave the 'Wee Frees' their historical
fame and which vested in this Union the bulk of the funds of the
old Free Church proper.

The House of Lords declared in August 1904 that those who
adhered to the Free Church were the 'True Free Church of
Scotland' and therefore the rightful owners of all the property
and funds.

This Union was heralded as one of the greatest blessings which
had come to Scotland for years.

There still remained another union to be formed, viz. : that
of the authentic Church of Scotland and the United Free Church
in 1929.

Originally the Bible, as we know it, was written by more than
thirty-five writers, distributed over sixteen centuries, and therefore
it was impossible for them to have a mutual understanding as to
the purpose of the Book and their own particular section as it was
related to the whole. Only a few of the writers of the Bible
were of sufficient scholarship to write ; the majority were un-
lettered and incompetent to write any manuscript. Time does
not leave its mark on this great work and so it retains its perennial
freshness.

The 'Unity' of the Bible is truly remarkable. Written, as I

have said, by some thirty-five different persons over some 1600 years ; written in many different languages in many different countries by people in every walk of life—herdsmen, fishermen, scribes, preachers, politicians. Written under all sorts of circumstances and conditions, yet all blending in unity of thought. One can only conclude by saying that all these writings were inspired by a Master-mind ; a Master-Architect.

Yes, indeed, all the Sundays spent at Croft Cottage were hours that could be looked upon with reverence ; none of us seemed to have a care in the world. They, and their godly neighbours—whom I got to know—were truly a great people. They had taken unto themselves for protection the Shield of Faith ; for up in the Highlands and Islands the congregations get strong advice from their preachers. The WORD must succeed where the SWORD failed ; and the ministers appear before men with an arresting 'Thus saith the Lord' ; and proclaiming that the Church of Christ in Scotland should always appear 'fair as the moon, clear as the sun, and terrible as an army with banners'.

In the Free, and Free Presbyterian Churches, one stands during prayers and remains seated whilst singing the Psalms to metre. There is no organ or musical instrument of any form in these churches. The singing is led by a precentor, and is of a depth that one seldom comes across in an English church ; and Psalms sung in Gaelic are profoundly impressive and heart-moving. I have said the people one meets in these islands and highlands of Scotland are all humble. As the lark that soars the highest builds her nest the lowest ; as the nightingale that sings so sweetly sings in the shade when all things rest ; as the branches that are most laden with fruit bend lowest ; as the ship most laden sinks deepest in the water—so those most holy are the humblest.

In these days of probing outer space and of men being shot into orbit, one wonders if theologians give thought to the possibility of there being life on other planets ? I am of opinion that many of the devout Highland folk do go *outside* space each time they are in earnest prayer—into the eternal realm, 'Heaven' ; for do they not believe in two worlds, spiritual and physical ; and in that belief there is surely immensity of space ?

Through the many centuries, of course, Christianity has had

many blows given it ; but it has more than weathered all such storms. It can be likened to the anvil in a blacksmith's shop, where if one looks in, one sees many worn-out old hammers lying around the floor. But peculiarly enough, the anvil never wears ; it is the other way about ; the anvil wears the hammers out. And so it is, the anvil of THE WORD which has been battered upon is unharmed. 'Tis the hammers that have perished.

These were days spent in love and contentment, surrounded with good-living folk, Fiona, Mother and Colin. The Bible and its teachings have lost nothing of their value with the passing millenniums—nothing. Other books fade and die, but THE BOOK and its message—so amply borne out by the Highlander—live on. People are rated higher than possessions with the true Highlander; and such good friends make the latitude and longitude of life. You can't sustain life by eating pound notes ; what really matters at all levels is not the money one earns, but what goods and services can be obtained in exchange for them ; what 'good-living' can be assimilated thereby.

These particular days of mine in Mull were a revelation ; and in them, and with such a wonderful household, I would in all humility quote chapter 21 of the Book of Revelations, viz., 'I saw a new heaven and a new earth' . . . in which I was now living.

With every tick of the clock the present becomes the past ; and whether we like it or not, we grow older with each tick. And also we grow in knowledge.

CHAPTER 17

GAIRLOCH

AFTER the Mod, the time for my departure was drawing rapidly to a close ; and both Fiona and I—as well as the family—were feeling Time was running out.

We had had many happy, very happy, days together ; we had fallen in love and become engaged ; but the parting—it gave us all aching hearts. But Fiona was a sensible, practical woman, and knew full well the saying '*que sera, sera*', as well as the Gaelic equivalent '*An Rud a Bhitheas Ann, Bitheas E Ann*'. I simply *had* to go north to Gairloch to get my house ready, so that one day it would be a fitting residence for my pearl, my fair queen in ophir gold, as I had previously termed her ; and it may be remembered I had said where the front door key could be found! It would take time to get things transformed and straightened out into the dream house I had planned. Fiona knew that.

I reminded her of a previous thought that had come to me in the Red Sea—of the story of Jacob's love for Rachel, one of the great idylls of literature. Rachel who was 'beautiful and well favoured', and of the long fourteen years Jacob waited. I told her I would wait for her to eternity ; to the day she could leave her mother and brother, and come to me, radiant and in perfect happiness of soul. And solemnly we pledged ourselves in this great love we had for one another. It was the greatest I had ever known.

Trusting each other, we never doubted the outcome, for we both knew this *was* the end of the rainbow. Fiona was everything a loving man could desire. How thankful I was that I had met her ; my other experiences abroad were figuratively centuries away.

I felt I had, in the words of Scripture, been 'born again', passing from the shadows of long ago into light and life.

It was all so wonderful ; all so inexplicable our meeting and our love. She was always as radiant as a Persian kitten; and her smile outshone all others, and twice blessed for the warmth it bestowed on me. Her eyes always shone with the untouched wonder of a child. She was as industrious as a beaver; and how she looked after the croft, her mother and brother was an inspiration to countless others. She had the sunniest approach to living of any woman I had met. To quote Esther, she had 'light and gladness and joy' in her heart to me.

Yes, this was *real* love; not just infatuation, for both of us had long passed that stage and age. She was, as the French would say, *joli à croquer*, 'sweet enough to eat'!

I draw a respectful blank over the scenes of my departure. Again, the French have an apt saying, *partir c'est mourir un peu*, 'to leave is to die a little'.

Goodbyes all round at Croft Cottage; Fiona waving me off at Tobermory pier; and thence to Gairloch, to another world that I hoped was to welcome her at a not too distant date.

And so,

> I went off to my land of dreams,
> Where Time stands still, or so it seems;
> Where the waves lap gently with a sigh
> From the island of Mull, and over the sky.

> To Ross-shire's heights and mighty Bens,
> Where the babbling streams sing through the glens;
> You find no crowds, and you find no wealth,
> But what you *do* find, is yourself.

> Life's major worries are sure to decrease
> Once in REAL love; for joy and peace
> Embracing the Future, the Present, and Past
> Enfolds your heart, whilst life doth last.

After two days I arrived safely at Gairloch, Wester Ross, staying at that renowned hotel I had patronised for nigh on fifty years. The Gairloch Hotel truly has an unrivalled outlook, commanding a beautiful situation close to the edge of the large horseshoe-shaped bay of Gairloch; looking over to the Isle of Skye, the Cuillins, and on clear days and nights, Stornoway in Lewis and the south end of Harris. The hotel is superbly decorated, has every comfort, first-class food and is very efficiently managed. In truth an ideal spot—peace and contentment personified. My house was full of workmen, with 'Charlie boy' as leading craftsman, seeing that masons, plumbers, plasterers, painters, electricians—and maybe a few others!—were satisfactorily getting on with their appointed tasks. In due course we had transformed it all from 'Log cabin to White House'; and after clearing away all the building debris, the next thing was to make the rough garden into landscape form; and this I did with the help of a young fellow near by, who seemed to be a veritable Hercules in the matter of handling massive boulders for the making of the rockeries. His name was John; a fine chap. He, and Alister from the Flowerdale Estate here, completely changed everything, bringing order out of chaos; a fitting tribute to them both.

GAIRLOCH. I have described this wonderful place, its lovable people, its great scenery—this altogether enchanting land—fully in *And It Came to Pass*, so it may be somewhat out of place to deal with same again, for it would take page upon page; although it *is* a beauty spot that can well bear recalling and retelling. It is a district set apart—God's own country I always term it. Artists have lavishly expended every variety and shade of colour to reproduce the grandeur of mountain scenes in all weathers; the heat-haze of summer rising off the purple-heathered moorlands, which in late August and September give the appearance of a carpet of spilt claret; and then later on, the bracken changing colours into red, yellow and brown.

There is no season of the year when nature stands still, or does not please the eye in Mull, the Islands, or Wester Ross.

One cannot absorb that strange atmosphere that evokes what the Gaels call the 'wave in the heart', or the 'dream in the eye', until, *and* until, one has lived in the Highlands, and come to know the place and the people.

> We're friendly people in Wester Ross;
> We laugh and chat, and none of us 'posh';
> We share our joys and sorrows too,
> And life is richer, because we do.
>
> Far from the noise and bustle of town
> We live our lives without renown;
> We do our work in a peaceful way,
> Helping each other day by day.

Those from the South say we're dull, I fear,
But *we* find bliss in all that's here ;
And when the tale of our life is told,
Some of the pages may shine like gold.

Yes, town life and the street one lives in appear in the Highlands to be an unreal background ; reality in the Highlands is
the scent of the wind, the ripple of the sea, the babbling of the
streams ('burns') as they flow towards the sea, chattering away
in Gaelic ; the sheep and the skipping lambs that one has to be
so careful of in motoring, the cows you suddenly come across at
the many blind corners, chewing their cud as if it were chewing-
gum, looking aimlessly at you and your car, and just—thinking!
hearing the call of the owl—the 'old woman of the night', as it is
termed in the Gaelic ; and the overwhelming significance of the
starry heavens.

In the towns and cities, man measures himself by his con-
structional works, of the improvements he makes, of scientific
advancement, and so on ; and boastfully prides himself on his
greatness in such achievements.   But up in the Highlands man is
completely dwarfed in his own importance by the mountains
and scenic wonders constantly surrounding him, and must
humbly stand aside in admitting the greatness of nature and of
an unseen architect.

Gairloch—the land of the *Fàiltes* and *Slàinte Mhaths* ; and
mentioned by that great geographer, Ptolemy of Alexandria, who
lived about A.D. 120.   I had long known and loved this part of
Ross-shire, having seen it in every month of the year, and yet even
now I find a new delight each day springing up in some shape or
form.   Search where you will in Britain you will not come across
such a rugged attractive coast-line with so uncrowded beaches on
such limitless golden stretches of sand ; a friendly people with
old-world Highland courtesy, charm and unbridled hospitality—
a hospitality that is not just a cliché : it is a way of life.

Here, indeed, one meets *real* Highlanders, dwelling in the
homes of their fathers and their fathers' fathers.   Here are nona-
genarians, octogenarians and a few youthful septuagenarians !
Friends all ; a great people ; and half the charm of living up in
these parts is in one's dealings with them.   And for the tourist,
what would a Highland holiday be, if it were not for the personal
contacts of the daily visit to the general stores for groceries or

K

haberdashery ; and to the post office for letters and fish! And if you keep your ears open, hear some gossip on the way. Their English is spoken with an exquisite intonation ; they have a courtesy and hesitant grace of manner peculiar to themselves that you never find in any other part of Britain. You never find a bombastic, loud-mouthed Highlander. But, alas! the Highlands are not a progressive area or community as we think of the term 'progress' in England. The population tends to dwindle away ; fewer and fewer speak the Gaelic tongue. But no matter what part of the Highlands you visit, no matter what religions they keep, Catholic, Free Presbyterian, Free Church, Church of Scotland, they have all held together in their trials and tribulations through the years ; and of course their records in the two World Wars cannot be surpassed.

Gairloch is 75 miles west of Inverness and 46 miles from Garve, where the whole scenery changes like a flash ; precipitous mountains loom ahead 'midst rugged beauty ; moorland stretching upon moorland. Verily a new world enters upon one's vision ; *and once you pass Garve, nobody hurries !* Gairloch may be said to commence at the post office, which is the hub of the local postal services. It is just near the old bridge, with the harbour and pier on the left, and on the right up the avenue of trees, Flowerdale House, which for long, long years has been the west-coast residence of the Baronets of Gairloch—the Mackenzies. The first laird was Hector Roy Mackenzie, born 1440, who succeeded to the title in 1494, and died in 1528. It was he who received a grant of Gairloch from King James IV in 1494. This old house of Gairloch was called AN TIGH DÌGE (moat house) from its having been surrounded by a ditch. The present house is called TIGH DÌGE NAN GORM LEAC (moat house of the blue flags, *i.e.* slates).

The name Gairloch is composed of two Gaelic words, *gearr*, meaning 'short', and *loch*. Gairloch is a very large Highland parish, for it covers an area of over 200,000 acres, and ranks as the fifth biggest parish in Scotland.

It is larger than the county of Rutland in England, and bigger than Clackmannanshire in Scotland. But the population is very small. The 1961 Census puts the figure as 1763.

The parish has a tremendous coast-line (said to be Europe's finest coast-line), very indented, possessing innumerable and lovely sandy beaches—all unrestricted.

There are more than twenty-three peaks of over 2000 feet in height ; five of them reaching over 3000 feet.

Taken as a whole the people's livelihood may be aptly put as 'one foot in the sea, and one foot on the shore' ; in other words, fishing and/or cultivating their bit of land.

In early days it was nothing for the young men to tramp on foot over to the east coast, Fraserburgh and such-like towns, to earn twelve weeks' money at the herring fishing ; then tramp all the miles back again in time to fish at this side of the coast. What a journey! And what stamina was required in those days in order to survive.

The Celtic inhabitants of the north-west Highlands have always been enthusiastic over *poetry* and *music*.

One, William Ross, was a very celebrated poet—or bard— and was universally known as 'The Gairloch Bard'.

He was born at Broadford in Skye in 1762. His mother was a native of Gairloch and daughter of the renowned blind piper and poet Iain Dall, also known as John Mackay. His father built a small house on Aird, the site of which, Leas-a-Rosaich, surrounded by rowan-trees, can still be pointed out. It was the headquarters of the Ross family from which they came and went ; and here it was that Ross died. He was educated in Forres and later joined his parents, who had moved to Gairloch. His father was a pedlar and young William went along with his father in his journeyings through Lewis and the Western Isles, and so became acquainted with the Gaelic language in all its different dialects. At the age of 24 he was put in charge of the Gairloch parish school and was most successful in his work there and his reputation grew. He studied Latin and Greek and became quite a master of those difficult languages. He acted as precentor in the Gairloch church. From his youth upwards he was never a robust lad, and he died in 1790 in Badachro, near Aird farm, at the early age of 28.

He was buried in the churchyard at Gairloch and it is recorded the whole population of the district were present to pay their last respects to a very clever man. He was of their race, their blood and bone. They knew and loved him well.

Many years later, in 1850, a handsome monument was erected over his grave through the efforts of Mr. George Ross, a clansman of his, who for many years was head keeper at Flowerdale House, Gairloch.

The monument bears inscriptions in both Gaelic and English and reads :

> In memory of *William Ross*, sometime schoolmaster of Gairloch, better known as the Gairloch bard, who died in 1790, aged 28 years, this monument is erected over his grave by a few of his countrymen and others headed by the amiable and accomplished proprietor of Gairloch, in testimony of their respect and admiration of his extraordinary genius and great native talent 1850.
>
> His name to future ages shall descend,
> While Gaelic poetry can claim a friend.

He was truly acknowledged as the foremost Gaelic scholar of his day, and his poetry, it is said, came from the heart.

Whilst in Gairloch—far away from Mull, it seemed—I heard regularly from Fiona. Her letters were full of loving thoughts ; always saying they were talking of me, and missing me tremendously. Mine to her were couched in similar vein. Temporarily I felt a void ; I knew it was only temporary, but I went about feeling I had lost my mate. When the ring-dove has lost its mate, it sits lone and brooding and will not be comforted. When the bird that hath been robbed of its young comes back again and again, and hovers with reluctant wing over the spot where her nest was built, she fills the hedge-rows with her plaintive cries. Such are the yearnings of nature. However, I was reassured in the full knowledge that Fiona would come to me whenever opportunity permitted ; but naturally her first duty was to look after her mother. They were all well.

The months went by ; and the years.

I was as happy as I could reasonably be in my house. I had kindly religious folk as neighbours. Religion plays a major part in this community's life ; and living with and amongst them all I, too, 'kept the Faith'. Up here in Wester Ross the Sabbath takes on a totally different sense and feeling to that experienced in England. Everyone else is keeping the day Holy. *That*, I think, is the key—the answer—to the difference down South, where people make Sunday a holiday outing in the car, or cut the grass ; buses run, and coaches make up so-called Sunday 'mystery tours'. There is none of that here. There is no '*movement*' to be seen or heard ; save the going to and from the kirk. This Scottish Highland heritage of keeping the Sabbath could very well be extended beyond the Highland boundaries.

A complete day of rest, relaxation and thought, enables one to start the week with a calm confidence. It is to be envied and copied. In short, the difference between the Sabbath here and the Sundays down in England, cannot be fully realised until—and until—you live here . . . 'keeping the Sabbath'.

Yes, I loved the life, but above all, missed Fiona. Whenever I had been away a day or so in the car, I was always glad to get home. I used to experience a certain glow within me as the car bounded and purred along. I felt myself scuttling through the bends and glens with the pleasurable assurance of a homeward-bound squirrel, always saying to myself that life lay around the next corner—to my dream house.

> Great is the joy in coming home,
> Rounding the corners without a groan ;
> Treading the path and gravel once more
> With your eager hand on the opening door.
>
> With the evening shadows upon the road
> One's shoulder needs to ease its load ;
> Then surely one's soul should be full and glad,
> For journey's end should not be sad.
>
> And with the last sign-post safely past
> One's heart should echo 'Home at Last' . . .

Yes, back to my dream house, where I knew one day Fiona would be, and remain as my wife, offering the sacredness of her love and her life to me for ever. She was my Rose of Sharon. Truly, the rose is sweet, yet it loses its smell ; but the lovely rose of Sharon grows sweeter and sweeter.

And so Time went by.

The earth continued to spin, and the sea rolled on incessantly and eternally. And our love ? it deepened and deepened. Although we were separated by miles of land and sea, yet many waters cannot quench love, neither can the floods drown it. All I was doing at my house and grounds at Gairloch was for love of Fiona ; it was to be our house of peace, love and contentment, for I had set myself as a seal upon her heart ; and as a seal, so too had Fiona set hers on mine. We were never disillusioned.

I thought of paying a fleeting visit to Mull ; but then, as there was no one to look after the house and garden here, it was difficult. There was always something to be done ; always something needing one's personal attention. All the yesterdays, todays and tomorrows seemed to bring their own quota of work. At one sermon I listened to in the Free Kirk, the minister told us that 'all our yesterdays, and all our tomorrows are with God. Only today was ours ; and not all of that guaranteed.' Would we not say then, indeed, at the beginning of each new day—as was said of old—'this is the day that the Lord hath given ; we will be glad and rejoice'.

Christmas came and Christmas went ; though up in the Highlands the majority only 'keep' the New Year ; and in olden times, New Year's Day used to be celebrated on the 12th January. Some Highlanders seem to keep it from the 1st to the 12th inclusive! As for myself, I kept both Christmas and New Year quietly; there were no church bells, of course, ringing out the glad tidings as in England, but e'en so, I recalled Longfellow's poem about the message of the Christmas bells, 'so that all the world might read from them, comfort' :

> God is not dead ; nor doth He sleep.
> The wrong shall fail, the right prevail
> With peace on earth, goodwill to men . . .

Aye, snow was upon the land, and I thought of Fiona having to prepare food and mash for the hens and the lone cow ; and of crofters in some of the out-of-the-way spots, living on salt herring and oatmeal. There was keen frost at nights, and in the morning one's footsteps took on a clear, crispy, resounding note. Snow was on the peaks, the haggis was on the boil and the hunter home from the hills, as I have said before. A blanket of whiteness cut off my house and the means of getting the car on the road. The whole countryside took on a magic of white wonderland : trees of rarest lace pattern ; sculptures of strange beauty were everywhere ; far-off glistening hills, and above all a 'stilly quietness'. In the evenings with a clear, frosty sky, a brilliant moon would rise and make its path vividly and placidly across the bay, throwing silvery streaks for all to see. At times a shooting star would flash across the heavens. At other times one bright star would appear, with timid ones following.

'If Winter comes, can Spring be far behind?' In March the days have lengthened ; the larch and the birch begin to herald spring ; and towards the end of May nature has begun its revival.

The cuckoo pays us its annual visit from across the ocean ; and we get bored with its constant song ; the bluebells of Scotland burst into bloom. In the springtime, a young man's fancy turns to love, 'tis said. But as to a crofter, he has work on his hands ; he is far too busy to be thinking of love. At the beginning of March he starts to turn over his land with the foot-plough— the *cas-chrom*—quite a tricky, primitive implement to handle. By the middle of April most of his spring work is done and then 'the peats' have to be cut—here again with a special cutting tool. *Peat*, the very name gives one the real smell o' the mystic isles and the north-west Highlands. It is the real crofter's main fuel. A very large part of Wester Ross is covered by peat bogs, and to the casual visitor these bog-lands with their characteristic vegetable life seem uninteresting except for just a passing glance, to say to their friends 'back home' they had seen 'peat growing' ! to say what a lovely smell pervades a room with a peat fire burning. Peat is evidently a post-glacial deposit, and in the long ages past with the weather cool and wet, the growth of 'sphagnum' moss would be encouraged, and this is the main formation of peat. So it grew and accumulated over the long, long years. Then fences to be seen to ; later on crops have to be reaped, potatoes lifted, out-houses repaired, drains 'sorted', and so on. Then there are of course the sheep to be cared for and rounded up by the crofter and his faithful collie. Some of these collies seem to have a hypnotic influence on sheep, getting them to do exactly what is required of them. A crofter with only a few sheep is really helpless without his collie. Lovely animals they are, sensing one's moods like a loving wife. It might be remarked that sheep do not sit about the hillside 'at random'. Scientists tell us they have a social behaviour of their own. Each sheep has his own patches of vegetation—known as 'rakes', over which it moves in regular daily fashion. So they are not so dumb as we would make them out to be ! There is never any rest for a crofter ; never a dull moment. So one can realise he has little or no time for courting, save in the winter !

As for myself, time was on my hands ; at any season of the year could I welcome Fiona. It was just a matter of waiting.

Spring turned into summer ; and a good summer in Gairloch can be a never-forgotten dream. The sun rises well to the north-east, passes right round the bay, and in late evening drops into

the sea behind Skye, like a red-hot ball of fire—'Trinidad Red'—
throwing up fantastic colours, lighting up the whole universe with
its auric glow. Then, after it has dipped, Apollo's sky chariot is
ready to start on its orbit through space again the following day ;
and the next day ; and the day after that—as has been the pattern
since these mountains were created. Surely—by faith—we must
be more than onlookers to manifestations of such precision ?
Surely some Divine thought must exist, moving ceaselessly ;
moving in such complete order and reason ? Day in and day out,
my own view from where I write these lines presents differing
pictures—captivating pictures. Scenery with a capital S ; from
Kilimanjaro-high to Trinidad red low.

And it is the same of Mull ; but Fiona would not see the
'massiveness' as is here in Wester Ross, where the whole surroundings are crashingly beautiful.

After dinner, on a fine, stilly evening in September, I took my
coffee, cigar and a 'Tia-Maria' liqueur, and sat on the garden seat
overlooking the bay admiring this gem of Wester Ross, situate
among such a living force as these Gaelic folk are ; glancing at
the rugged coast-line, and witnessing the varied beauty of colour
and form of the mountains of Torridon, Applecross and the
Cuillins of Skye ; uplifting mountains which at times seem near
enough to touch ; muscat-purple mountains against a sky of rose,
crimson and gold. The Torridon mountains are the oldest in the
world ; they were old before the Himalayas even started. All
these mountains are rich indeed in impact value. The whole
possessed an atmosphere of the old world, with a crescent moon
about to rise. Over twenty-five years ago, under the same
moon, I had—like David of old—been greatly afflicted. But
we are told 'all things work together for good'. A few of the
rose petals of April 1937 were between the leaves of Hebrews,
chapter 11, in my old Bible. They were now dried and withered.
The 'life' in the enamel box of the Pharaoh age had gone for
ever. Having grown older—conjointly with my friends—I
think of medical science attempting to squeeze more and more
years into life ; yet there is, as yet, no sign of the Elixir of
Youth ; and the eternal search for Shangri-La goes on. As the
years multiply, the milestones become gravestones, and under
each a friend. In spite of the latest wonders—deep-freeze sleep,

and 'spare parts' for the human frame—the chances are that many of us *will* grow old ; then die. But old age is not all loss ; far be it, for the gains which ageing bring lie more in the realms of the mind and of the emotions. Ancient Greece and Rome knew all about that.

Feeling in reminiscent mood, I went indoors for more coffee and another cigar. I set about thinking of some of the special events in my crowded and varied life : of going abroad in 1914 ; of Marcelle and a most engaging career and wonderful twenty-three years in the Isle of Delight and of seeing the holiest mountain in the world—Adam's Peak, Ceylon, and the Temple of the Great Buddha at Kandy ; of Hong Kong's peak (1800 feet high), gazing down on the twinkling fairyland of that harbour, and of Kowloon across on the mainland of China ; of Singapore, sitting lazily on the verandah of the great Raffles Hotel watching all the world go by ; of Italy and Naples, my footsteps sinking in the molten lava on the lip of the crater of mighty Vesuvius, ever belching forth acrid smoke, fire and brimstone within a few yards of me, and with hessian bags covering me to prevent the sparks and red-hot sulphurous dust burning my clothes—and the ruins of ancient Pompeii ; of Aden, pondering over the age and workmanship of Solomon's biblical water-tanks ; of Egypt, Tháfne and the pyramids ; of Tangier and the native Kasbah ; of Gibraltar and its giant rock, and its famous legendary monkeys ; of Malta, looking at Michelangelo's great painting in the cathedral there of Salome's dance and the beheading of John the Baptist (St. Matthew, chapter 14) ; of Bali in Java, where the native women wear not a stitch of clothing ; of Calcutta and the sacred Ganges ; of Bombay and the Tower of Silence, with vultures constantly hovering around, darting down devouring the carcases of dead Parsees ; of Penang and the snake temple with its hundreds of yellow snakes lying around, hopelessly doped ; of the south of France, its merriment on carnival days, and of its casinos ; and of England—the white cliffs of Dover.

And then back again to earth on the magic carpet ; back to Mull and hearing the cry of the seagulls flying low over Tober-mory bay, and thinking of my first meeting with Fiona and of the superlative days spent at Croft Cottage, with all four of us sitting round the peat fire there, on chilly or wet autumn even-ings, talking and talking, until the red fire went out of the peat, and the sun rose next morning ! And finally back to seeing the fishing-boats coming in to Gairloch bay. In all this, I seemed to have touched the Alone—alone.

For well over a decade I had been 'searching'; searching at times for the truth within myself, and in the end I found it, not in myself, but in another—Fiona. When you find *that* in someone else, you instinctively give everything you've got—everything. And that makes for enduring happiness. Christianity tells us there was nothing in the beginning, only thought. And so our lives are what our thoughts make them.

It was late—nearly midnight—though there were still shafts of colour in the sky ; and I felt exhausted in my tour. Being too tired to take a bath I just tumbled into bed. And softly the leaves of memory fell away in the comforting, exquisite verses of the Song of Songs, which is Solomon's :

Rise up, my love, my fair one, and come away.
For, lo! the winter is past, the rain is over and gone ;
The flowers appear on the earth ; the time of the singing birds
  is come, and the voice of the turtle is heard in our land. . . .
Until the day break, and the shadows flee away. . . .

I was wakened by what I thought was a knock at my bedroom door ; opening my eyes and half asleep, I reached for my glasses, and could see it was daylight. The clock on my bedside table pointed to 8 a.m. A knock ? it couldn't be, for I had locked up, and none of my neighbours ever came around visiting me at such an untimely hour. I must have been dreaming ; so I snuggled under the bedclothes again, saying to myself it was too early to get up just then. I would have another wee doze.

Another knock, and in a drowsy, husky voice, I heard myself saying—I don't know why—'Come in'.

I could hear the door opening over the thick carpet, and the rustling of feet. I looked up.

'Fiona.'

'Yes, sweetheart, it's me ; I've come!'

'Darling, it's you! How did you get in ?' 'The key, . . .' she said, but I interrupted any further words by springing up and kissing her, as I held her in my arms. 'Darling, is it *really* you ?' 'Yes, dear, just me' . . . 'And, Mother ?' I said, 'is she . . .' ; I was afraid to go on, thinking the worst might have happened ;

but Fiona, sensing what was in my mind, said, 'No, pet, she's fine ;
and so is Colin ; but I'll tell you everything over breakfast, as
soon as you're up and dressed.'

I dashed out of bed shouting, 'The tea's on the sill near the
kettle, and the bacon and eggs are in the frig. ; and I'll be with
you in a matter of minutes!'

CHAPTER 18

RAINBOW'S END

At breakfast I listened to all that had happened, which had
enabled Fiona to come to me.

It would appear Colin had been offered a post in the
Forestry Department on the mainland, with offices at Invergarry,
seven miles south of Fort Augustus, where—along the Caledonian
Canal area—there was a deal of reafforestation taking place; and
Mother had gone to live with a widowed sister at Fort William,
which was only twenty-five miles from Colin's office, so he could
always manage home each night. Fiona had stayed behind in
Mull for a time to see to the selling up of the croft, the cow and
the hens. And they had been fortunate to get a near relative to
take over everything.

She purposely told me none of this in her letters, she said, until
all had been finalised ; and besides, she added, 'I wanted to spring
a surprise on you, Stanley.'

'Well, that's great news,' I said. 'The search is ended, Fiona.'
'Yes, dearest, the search is over,' she replied, her eyes filling with
tears of joy. The journey was ended, the summit attained, the
barriers fallen. *Que sera, sera.*

'And of course,' I added, 'Fort William is not so far away, so
we can always run down and see how everybody is getting along,
and cheer them up.' 'How wonderful you are, darling ; you
think of everything,' she said.

And that we did, very soon ; for we had a pressing 'date' to
keep in Edinburgh, to which Mother could offer no excuse this
time in absenting herself ; nor could Colin.

It was a quiet wedding, with no one except Fiona's closest
relatives present—for I was the last of my family tree ; the last of

he Mohicans! Mother looked sweet and younger than ever ; ˈiona looked radiant ; Colin immaculate in his kilt ; and as for nyself—well, I was only the groom!

For Fiona and myself it was *Banais nam Bliadhna* (the wedding ˈf the year) ; the most colourful rainbow of our lives. In truth, ˈt had come to pass. Life at times can be truly shattering, and yet, ˈt times, most rewarding. Now, in Arabic, it was *tammam*, ˈperfect'.

Fiona—my Aphrodite, goddess of love—and I are wonderfully ˈappy ; it could not have been otherwise. And readers who nay have closely read these pages will, I am sure, echo 'No, it ˈould not have been otherwise.'

'QUE SERA, SERA.'
'OTI EÍNÉ NA GÍNNI, THA GÍNNI.'
'ZEI MA TÍGI, TÍGI.'
'AN RUD A BHITHEAS ANN, BITHEAS E ANN.'
'Whatever will be, will be.' . . .

After a prolonged honeymoon in Southern Ireland (including ˈ visit to Blarney Castle, five miles out of Cork, to kiss the magical ˈtone of Eloquence!) we returned to the Dream House at Gair-ˈoch. As I have said elsewhere, we have suffered no disillusion-ˈnents ; age has not withered, nor have the years condemned our ˈreat love.

In the Gaelic we wish all those we know, and all those we ˈon't know—readers of this book wherever you may be—*Slàinte Nach Teirig!* ('Here's health everlasting to you.')

THE END (of the rainbow)

READER'S MEMOS